MW00635945

NO *Turning* BACK

© 2020 by TGS International, a wholly owned subsidiary of Christian Aid Ministries, Berlin, Ohio.

All rights reserved. No part of this book may be used, reproduced, or stored in any retrieval system, in any form or by any means, electronic or mechanical, without written permission from the publisher except for brief quotations embodied in critical articles and reviews.

ISBN: 978-1-950791-53-8

Cover and text layout design: Kristi Yoder

Published by:
TGS International
P.O. Box 355
Berlin, Ohio 44610 USA
Phone: 330.893.4828
Fax: 330.893.2305
www.tgsinternational.com

NO *Turning* BACK

Pablo Yoder

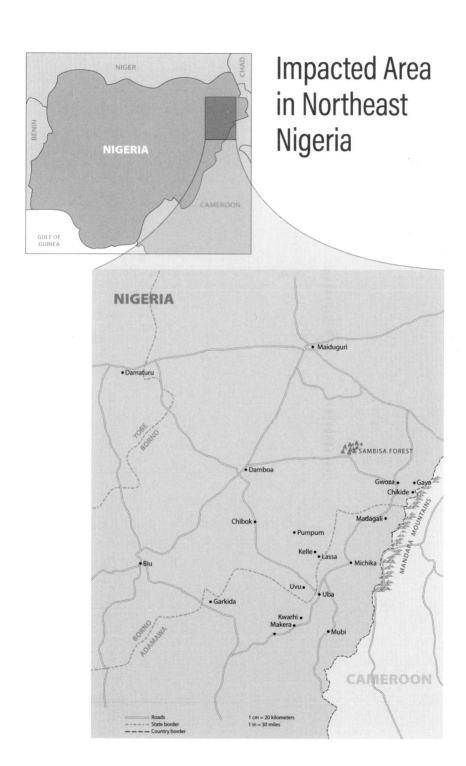

Impacted Area in Northeast Nigeria

v

Dedication

Keila, my dear granddaughter, I dedicate this book to you.

Keila, though you are still young, I firmly believe that you, like many young women of northeast Nigeria, will choose to follow Jesus. Only God knows what your life will be like as you tiptoe into adulthood, or what following Jesus might cost you, or what rewards it may bring.

And Keila, I can't wait until you and I, and all the rest of God's children from Africa and all over the world, will meet at Jesus' feet at the threshold of God's throne to praise HIM forever!

Meet you there, Keila dear!

Table of Contents

Preface

The huge Guanacaste tree's silhouette draped out over the pond like some giant umbrella in the ethereal predawn light. A gentle fog lent softness to the scene, giving it an eerie touch. As I sat at my prayer window, preparing my heart for my own special time with my Creator, I gazed at the lovely picture outside my window. *So much beauty,* I sighed. *So lovely! Thank you, Lord. Thank you!*

Then, almost involuntarily, "Lord, you know I need a title for my book." The little prayer tumbled right out of my heart with the hint of a sigh. "I know you won't fail me. In your time."

My wife and I had just returned from Nigeria, Africa, after doing research for this book. My heart was full, bursting at the seams. Churning in my innermost being were the testimonies of my dear African brothers and sisters who were willing to follow Jesus no matter what the cost—be it terrible suffering or even death. I couldn't wait to get to my writing, but the title remained elusive.

Several days earlier I had told my children several of the stories, sometimes with tears running down my cheeks. My son Jacinto had suggested, "Dad, the title should be something about being willing to follow Jesus—something like 'To Follow Jesus' Footsteps.' "

Jacinto's suggestion got my mind scouting in the right direction, but I wasn't quite satisfied. And that's why "Help me, Lord!" became the cry of my heart as I pondered a title.

Later that morning, Sim Yoder, a dear Georgia brother, shared a song with me. Sim posts a song a day on a WhatsApp group I am part of. On that particular morning the song was "I Have Decided to Follow Jesus." It's a song I sang in Sunday school when I was a boy.

I would have promptly forgotten the sweet song if Sim hadn't also included a story of the song's origin. After reading the story, two things were immediately clear. First, this touching story was very much like some of the testimonies I had just gleaned from northeast Nigeria. And second, I had the perfect title for my book! "Thank you, God!"

Here is the story Sim sent me, in my own words.

The Last Words of a Martyr

As the eerie evening shadows stretched eastward, the western sky was turning the color of a ripe papaya—as if it were blushing at what was about to happen. There was no breeze, and a solemn hush had fallen upon the crowd that had gathered in a circle around the square of a small village in northern India.

The village chief's piercing voice rang out, breaking the dreadful silence as he flung his horrific question at the man kneeling in front of him. "Jayesh, will you or won't you renounce Christ this evening? This is your last chance."

At the center of the plaza, a family huddled together,

kneeling in a straight line. Their hands were tied behind their backs. Their heads were bowed. They didn't make a sound until the chief's question was hurled at the man who knelt between his wife and his two sons. In a quiet but decided voice, Jayesh replied, "I have decided to follow Jesus. There is no turning back."

The chief's face contorted in anger. He nodded to a dozen archers who stood in a row behind the family. "The children," he commanded.

In an instant the archers released a dozen arrows that riddled the boys' bodies. Slowly they slumped to the ground.

"What do you say now?" the chief asked, hateful glee written all over his face.

"The cross is before me, but the world is behind me," Jayesh sobbed.

Nodding to the archers, the chief hissed, "The wife!"

After seeing his wife pierced by the arrows, Jayesh was given one more chance. He did not waver as he replied, "Though no one is here to go with me, I will still follow Jesus."

The chief nodded to the archers and Jayesh followed his family into glory.

The villagers who had crowded around were shocked into silence. They quietly slunk away, slipping into their bungalows. They felt ashamed at the chief's cruelty. The sacred scene of watching a family's loyalty and their willingness to die for their faith in the Lord Jesus had touched their hearts permanently.

It was in the late 1800s when a Welsh missionary first preached the Good News in this small village, which was steeped in Hinduism. Jayesh and his family were the first converts. Thankfully, their death was not the end of the story.

Years went by. The Welsh missionary and other Christians came to the village again and again to tell the people more about Jesus. Eventually a revival broke out in the village and even the chief and several of the archers were converted. Someone remembered Jayesh's last words and told them to the Welsh missionary. He passed them on to Sunder Singh, a well-known Indian evangelist and song writer, who put the words to traditional Indian music. The song immediately became popular in Indian churches, and eventually became a well-known song all over the world.

I Have Decided to Follow Jesus

I have decided to follow Jesus;
I have decided to follow Jesus;
I have decided to follow Jesus;
No turning back, no turning back.

The cross before me, the world behind me;
The cross before me, the world behind me;
The cross before me, the world behind me;
No turning back, no turning back.

Though none go with me, still I will follow;
Though none go with me, still I will follow;
Though none go with me, still I will follow;
No turning back, no turning back.

The best part of our trip to Nigeria in 2018 was hearing the stories of the many Christians who had suffered so bravely under the terror of Boko Haram. Yet we were also reminded of the sad reality that some Christians failed.

Humans fail. Only in heaven will we be perfect . . .

But many Nigerian Christians stood bravely, victoriously, refusing to renounce Christ and refusing to bow to Islam. Hundreds of them died for their faith. Their testimonies will be an encouragement and a blessing to Christians everywhere.

The biggest problem in writing this book was getting enough information. We interviewed dozens of Christians, but most of the interviews were fairly short. Some of the stories were heard only from a relative. For example, except for one who escaped, I was not able to interview the Chibok girls who were held captive in the Sambisa Forest personally—only their close relatives.

The question is, how can an author write a complete story with such short interviews? How can a foreigner, even if he spent three weeks in the country, write about things he knows so little about?

Though the basic facts are true as told to me by my dear Nigerian friends, some of the minor details may not always be quite accurate. And as my dear Nigerian readers will sense, though the author did the best he could, not all the details will ring clear to their culture.

In spite of all this, I trust that reading these powerful testimonies will enrich your Christian life and help you stay true to God during your own unique set of trials.

To God be all the honor!

Pablo

Introduction

The verdant jungle, usually a bedlam of sound and movement, was silent. Too silent.

Not a leaf shivered. Not an animal stirred among the jumble of vines and bromeliads that choked the jungle's canopy. Even the birds were quiet.

Only the jungle floor was active. Very active. It was war!

I stood perfectly still on the hilltop in the jungle and stared. The drama I witnessed was something so new, so astounding, and so terrible that I didn't know what to do—except stare.

For the first time in my life I was seeing an army of ants on the warpath. A fifty-foot-wide swath of the terrible warriors, flashing their long, sharp mandibles, marched toward me over the jungle floor. The mass of ants marched forward, always forward, seeking prey among the dead leaves and rotten logs.

What I didn't know at the time was that the swath of advancing army ants could well be up to three hundred feet long and several million ants strong. I only knew that never before had I seen so many ants in one place. Never before had I seen an army marching forward so relentlessly and with such a purposeful drive. No wonder the jungle was shocked to silence and sent to hiding!

As the ants worked their way toward me, I noticed groups of ants clustered together among the steady flow of marching warriors. Bending over, I used the several minutes I had left until they would start climbing up my pant legs to take a small stick and push the ants aside to see what made them cluster. Even as I uncovered their victim—an unfortunate katydid—I knew what I would find. Dozens of the ants were already dismembering poor Katy. They were doing what ants do best: devouring their prey!

I stepped back several steps and shook my head in wonder. *This is nature,* I thought. *It is unique and incredible in its design. Marvelous and wonderful in its perfection. Terrible and astounding in its reality.*

It was many years after this that I visited Nigeria. My wife and I spent a week in the city of Jos, in central Nigeria, listening to the stories of people who had been displaced by the attacks of Boko Haram in the northeastern part of the country. We then spent another week farther north, in the affected area, again interviewing people and hearing their stories of suffering.

Listening to the stories, I was reminded of that day in the jungle when I had seen those army ants. Except now it wasn't ants. It was an army of humans—Boko Haram—marching across the land. Slowly but surely, relentlessly and aggressively, they consumed everything in their path.

Army ants don't pardon anything in the jungle. Insects, invertebrates, arthropods and their larvae, earthworms, small snakes, and even baby animals and birds—all are fair game for the ants. I saw some creatures escape, but only those that could fly or run fast enough to stay ahead of those horrible mandibles.

The Boko Haram terrorists were more selective. They pardoned most Muslims in their raids southward—at least at first. It was the Christians that Boko Haram devoured most ruthlessly, usually killing any of the men who would not renounce Christ. The ones who did renounce Christ were trained to join their brutal ranks. They kidnapped the wives and children, holding them in their camps as slaves. They looted the Christians' businesses and houses, then burned them to the ground. They especially targeted the churches. In a Satan-inspired rage, they burned over a thousand Christian church houses in northeast Nigeria during 2013 and 2014.

Because God helps His children, many of them escaped. Much like the crickets in the jungle during the ant raid, the Christians scrambled ahead of the army, and God delivered them.

Most of the Christians did not fight back. This book tells their stories—how they had to suffer, flee from city to city, and be willing at any time to die for their faith. There are also stories of how God delivered so many of His own.

My wife and I interviewed dozens of Christians. We listened and watched, often shaking our heads incredulously at the sad, yet triumphant stories. *This is real persecution,* I realized. *This is war between good and evil. Between God and Satan.* It was terrible and astounding in its reality.

"Lord, have mercy!" my wife and I whispered again and again, with tears streaming down our cheeks. "Lord, have mercy. And thank you, God, for the many Christians you have delivered from the mandibles of the dreadful Boko Haram!"

Chapter 1

Tumba

Part one

To Live or to Die

The bright African sun had just gone into full blaze when the three young men hit the trail that meandered around the gnarled trees sprinkled across the powder-dry savanna. A flock of red-billed hornbills chattered in a baobab tree that drooped its short, twisted branches across the trail. As the young men approached, the birds squawked boisterously, throwing themselves into the morning air and flying clumsily across the red plain looking for a safer perch.

The young men were typical African youth, dressed like the farmers they were, with sandaled feet, simple threadbare trousers, and light sleeveless shirts. Tumba Tizhe, carrying a machete and a clay jug of water, took the lead. His face showed little emotion. Yakubu, Tumba's friend, smiled as he followed. Yakubu was the friendly type. The two had been friends for a long time and were both twenty-one years old.

Last in line was Gambo, who was leading two white plow cows. Gambo was not as outgoing as Yakubu, nor as pensive and quiet as Tumba. A serious-minded young man, he was a Christian on fire for the Lord.

"Do you think we will finish plowing the farm plot today?" Yakubu asked Tumba, adjusting the sack of tiny Irish potatoes he was carrying along for seed.

"Sure hope so," answered Tumba. "We're a little late this morning, but if we stick to it we should be done before sunset."

Gambo was just ready to reply when a sound brought them to a sudden halt. Motorcycles! Within seconds, the roar increased as the motorcycles came rapidly down the trail toward them. There was no time to react. As the cycles came into view, the young men's hearts froze. *Boko Haram!* The thought struck all three of them with frightening reality. Boko Haram soldiers often drove around on motorcycles doing their pillaging, but they usually hit at night, not in the morning.

"There's no time to run!" Tumba hissed.

The swarm of seven overloaded motorcycles quickly came to a stop, creating a cloud of dust as they surrounded the three young men. Each motorcycle carried two or three soldiers dressed in fatigues. All toted AK-47 assault rifles and had long knives at their waists.

"Hands up!" the leader of the group barked. "And no tricks, you pack of infidels. You are going with us."

Four of the soldiers lined up the three young men and told them to place their hands behind their backs. They tied their wrists together with string that made Tumba wince as it bit into his skin. After giving the four soldiers some quick instructions, the leader and the rest of the men jumped back on the cycles and roared away across the savanna. One of the remaining soldiers shouldered the sack of potatoes and the water jug while another grabbed the cows' ropes that dangled limply onto the red dirt. The other two soldiers stepped in behind the captives and yelled, "March!"

What would my mother say if she knew? Tumba wondered sadly as they hiked past the farm plot they had planned to plow. *Who knows when she will find out what happened?*

Tumba was from a distant town called Michika and was with his friend Yakubu because work was scarce in his hometown. After he and his family decided to try their luck in Lassa, a Muslim landowner gave them work on his farm where he raised maize, guinea corn, groundnuts, and Irish potatoes.[1] Tumba was delighted because he loved to farm, and now he could make a little cash as well.

Since Tumba and Yakubu were Christians, they had become fast friends with another Christian worker called Gambo during the three months of working on the farm. During this time they had lived with Gambo's family and gone to an EYN[2] church with him. Now the three were trekking north, not as fast as the Boko Haram soldiers wanted, but as fast as the two plow cows allowed them.

The next two days were terrible. Whenever the Boko Haram soldiers stopped to eat, they rudely stuffed several dates into the three captives' mouths. Dates were a main source of food for the terrorists because they were nourishing but didn't weigh much or take up much space. Occasionally the soldiers allowed them to take sips from their precious water jug.

Walking with their hands tied behind their backs was no fun. Tumba's wrists were now beyond regular pain. They had acquired a numb, intense throb that meant the blood was not circulating and the string was digging deeper into his now swollen hands. Although he could not see them, Tumba was sure his hands had turned purple. *I can't stand this awful pain much longer,* he cried inwardly.

---

[1] Corn, sorghum, peanuts, and regular potatoes, respectively.

[2] *Ekklesiyar yan'uwa a Nigeria,* (Church of Children of the Same Mother of Nigeria). EYN are the church's initials after it received its independence from the Church of the Brethren in 1972. The EYN church reportedly now has nearly a million members throughout Nigeria.

The EYN church teaches Jesus' command to love our enemies. As a result, there are many Christians in Nigeria who don't resist with violence even when they are killed for their faith. Most of the people interviewed for this book are members of the EYN church.

But Tumba and his friends did stand the pain. There were no other options. The cursing group of unhappy and bitter guards was not to be messed with.

Nights were the worst. Their hosts usually found an empty house where the captives were told they could lie down to rest. In spite of being fed a handful of dates before retiring, hunger assaulted them like a sledge-hammer. Catching little snatches of sleep was all they could do as their wrists throbbed in pain. They were not allowed to talk to each other. *I guess all we can do is think and pray,* thought Tumba.

Praying was not easy for Tumba. His pain was unbearable. So instead of praying, he cried quietly in the dark of the night, hoping his friends would not notice his weakness.

Praying was not something Tumba had done regularly. *Yakubu and I are not like Gambo,* he realized. *He is the praying type. He is always so excited about being a Christian. I wish I were more like him. I have been way too careless in my Christian life. I am sure he is praying fervently right now.*

During the second night, Tumba was afraid he would lose his mind because of the pain. Escaping was not an option. The four soldiers took turns staying awake all night long, cradling their AK-47s in their laps and keeping their eyes on the captives. In this way, the nights seemed even longer and deadlier than the days.

On the third day, Tumba noticed the terrain was getting steeper. They had left the savannas behind and were now hiking through what looked like foothills, and the hills above them were covered with a thicker stand of trees. Brush, choked with vines and thorns, hedged both sides of the trail, often reaching out and snagging the young men's tattered trousers. Though he didn't look, Tumba knew his legs were bleeding.

By midmorning, the captives could hardly go anymore. Tumba felt as if he could faint, and a mild fever was creeping over his whole being. Chills racked his tired body, and hunger and thirst weren't even an issue anymore. "I'm going to die!" he groaned, placing one foot in front of the other mechanically. Even the soldiers were tired and silent.

Suddenly the group of men stumbled into what appeared to be a little village. Mud huts and even some concrete houses were nestled among the forest of trees. The four soldiers were received with cheers as a group of men rushed out to meet them. As the men looked the prisoners over, they chatted with each other in the Hausa language, which the three captives understood.

Tumba noticed dozens of women, girls, and children watching in the background. He wondered if he would recognize any of them. *They are captives,* he realized. *And now, like it or not, we are also part of this group. I wonder if those girls aren't the Chibok girls who were kidnapped several months ago.* Too tired and sick to look around, Tumba and his two friends squatted under a tamarind tree as they waited for instructions.

The three young men were finally led to a medium-sized, dark man dressed in impeccable Nigerian army clothes, with a headband tied around his army cap. *That's the symbol of Boko Haram,* Tumba knew. *I sure don't like the looks of him! He looks as mean as any criminal.*

The leader sat on a chair surrounded by soldiers in front of the biggest building in the village. Tumba knew he was the village emir.[3]

This is one of Boko Haram's leaders, he realized, trembling in fright.

As the four tired soldiers disappeared into the village, the emir clucked at a fresh set of soldiers who stood at his service. Then he commanded, "Follow me and bring the boys."

The emir led the little band deeper into the forest. As they followed, Tumba knew the real test was coming. His heart trembled as tears pushed at his eyelids. In his fear of what lay ahead, he almost forgot his throbbing wrists, which were now a mass of putrid infection. *Either I live or I die,* Tumba realized with a dreadful reality. *It's up to me. They are going to ask me to renounce Christ. What shall I do?*

---

[3] A Muslim chief.

Tumba had already made his decision.

As they approached a little clearing, he knew two things beyond a shadow of a doubt. First, they were in the hands of a notoriously cruel Boko Haram emir, and if they didn't renounce Christ they would soon be dead men. Second, this camp was in the dreadful Sambisa Forest.

If there was ever a place that made the hearts of the people of Nigeria tremble, it was the Sambisa Forest. A 320-square-mile nature reserve in Borno State, the forest is about forty miles southeast of Maiduguri, the capital of Borno State.

In itself, the Sambisa Forest is not such a terrible place. It is a land of sparse forest, barren wilderness, and harsh countryside, with a sprinkling of villages around its edges. In 1970 it was set aside to be a nature reserve so tourists could experience the African jungle and enjoy its flora and fauna. On safaris, tourists could sometimes see baboons, patas and tantalus monkeys, common duikers, red-fronted gazelles, hartebeests, African leopards, spotted hyenas, and many other creatures.

After 1991, the forest was no longer managed properly, and things started going downhill. In 2013 Boko Haram insurgents took over the Sambisa Forest, leading to the gradual disappearance of its animals and its attractiveness.

Like the Garden of Eden, the Sambisa Forest was no longer a paradise. When the dark forces took control, it became a sinister labyrinth of chaos, a real devil's hideout. It was the perfect place for Boko Haram terrorists to live, hide, and call home.

NO TURNING BACK

Part two

Will You Renounce Christ?

"*Allahu Akbar!*"[1] If ever a phrase made the hearts of the Christians in Nigeria tremble, it was this one. And that's what the emir of Sambisa Forest yelled now as he paced back and forth in front of the three kneeling captives who hung their heads in dread. *"Allahu Akbar!"*

These were words every Muslim used many times, every day of his life. Tumba knew the meaning well—"Allah is the greatest!"

"My name is Abubakar Shekau, and I am the leader of Boko Haram."

Abubakar licked his lips, then sneered. "I can't understand why you Christians don't catch on!" he shouted, his eyes aflame. "Allah is the only true God. And we, Boko Haram, are bringing a revival to the Islamic religion. We are bringing the people back to the true Sharia law, to strict adherence to the Koran and what God taught us through his prophet Muhammad. We are the true children of God. You Christians are infidels."

Abubakar paused to let his words sink in. "Today is your chance to convert to the only true religion. We don't like to kill people. But as the Koran instructs us, if the infidels refuse to convert, they deserve to die."

---

[1] *Allahu Akbar* means "Allah is the greatest."

Abubakar placed himself right in front of the young men. Pointing at Tumba who knelt first in line, he continued. "What is your name?"

"Tumba Tizhe," Tumba answered.[2]

"So, you were the third born in your family and your father was a firstborn, eh?" Abubakar joshed, trying to keep the atmosphere light. "Today I change your name. Your name will be Ali, a good Islamic name that will be yours for the rest of your life."

Tumba was afraid to show his disapproval. He was proud of his real name and the connection it gave him to his father, who had died many years before. He didn't dare admit it, but he despised his new name. It seemed half of the Muslims he knew were named Ali.

Then, pointing at Yakubu, Abubakar asked, "What is your name?"

"Yakubu," was the lame answer.

"Yakubu is a Christian name," Abubakar spat. "I hate that name! From now on your name will be Habu, also a good Islamic name that will make you proud."

Turning to Gambo, the last in the line, Abubakar barked, "And what is your name?"

"Gambo," was the third prisoner's answer.

"Today I change it to Ibrahim," Abubakar demanded. "Today you will become a son of Islam, and you will be proud of your new name."

Everyone was startled when Gambo answered quietly, but firmly. "I reject that name. I am a Christian."

Suddenly Abubakar was angry—furiously angry. Taking a chair his servants brought him, he sat down and asked with an icy voice, "You, Ali," he said, looking at Tumba, "will you renounce Christ?"

Tumba nodded.

"Here, come to me," he said in a kinder tone.

Once Tumba stood in front of the leader, Abubakar motioned to one

---

[2] *Tumba* means "third born" in the Hausa language, and the last name is always the father's name. *Tizhe* means "firstborn," so Tumba was the third born of the firstborn.

of the soldiers, "Cut his bonds."

It wasn't easy for the soldier to cut the string that was by now deeply imbedded in Tumba's swollen wrists. But suddenly Tumba's arms fell free. Though he had lost most of the feeling in his arms and hands, a sharp pain went through him as the soldier ripped the strings from the deep gorges in his wrists. A putrid odor enveloped the group as the infected pus oozed out.

Turning, Abubakar looked at Yakubu. "Habu, will you renounce Christ?"

Yakubu nodded.

"You may come."

After his shackles were cut, Tumba saw right away that Yakubu's hands were not nearly as damaged as his own. *Why did they tie my hands so much tighter than his?* he wondered. *I'm not sure I'll ever be able to use my hands again.*

"Ibrahim, will you renounce Christ?" Abubakar barked, turning his attention to Gambo. His eyes burned like fire.

Gambo raised his head, and Tumba and Yakubu saw tears in the eyes of the brave young man they had met at the produce fields in Lassa. Clearly and boldly, Gambo spoke. "I will not renounce Jesus. He is my Lord and my Savior."

Abubakar jumped to his feet in a rage. Motioning to one of his men, he watched with a devilish grin as the soldier approached Gambo from behind with his knife in hand. Gambo didn't budge. The soldier grabbed him by his hair and jerked his head backward, exposing his throat. In a moment it was over. Gambo fell backwards, landing on his back, his legs buckling under him.

Abubakar turned on his heel and commanded the two remaining captives, "Follow me. We need to get you boys to our hospital so they can take care of your wounded wrists." Tumba and Yakubu followed numbly. As they stumbled through the forest, Tumba suddenly realized he was trembling from head to toe. *Gambo is the fortunate one,* he thought numbly. *He is with Jesus forever. Why am I such a coward?*

A pitiful, croaking cry emanated from the depths of Tumba's soul. *God, forgive me! God, forgive me! Oh God, please forgive me!*

This day in May 2014 was a day of choices. Gambo went home to be with Jesus, while Yakubu and Tumba chose to become Muslims.

It was a blessed day for Gambo. His problems were over forever.

It was a sad day for Tumba and Yakubu. Their problems had only begun.

Part three
In the Sambisa Forest

"*Allahu Akbar! Allahu Akbar! Allahu Akbar!*"

The rasping voice of the morning prayer call woke Tumba abruptly. He turned over onto his back slowly, his thin blanket clinging to his body. *What an unearthly hour to force a person to pray,* he groaned inwardly, his body screaming for more sleep. *But I must wake up. I must show these hard masters that I am a genuine Muslim now. My survival in this place depends on me being able to convince them that I am not a Christian anymore.*

Tumba's wrists were slowly healing. It had been a month since he had renounced Christ and started taking daily treatments at Boko Haram's makeshift hospital in the Sambisa Forest. The hospital was a simple concrete house set up as a crude clinic, with cots for the sick to lie on. Tumba found himself surrounded with wounded Boko Haram soldiers and an occasional sick captive. The nurses and doctors were all part of Boko Haram, and were trained to kill or to heal, depending on what their leaders dictated.

Because of Tumba's infected wrists, they were not yet pressuring him to become a warrior like most of the other men who had renounced Christ. So far they had allowed him to take it easy as he healed, except for errands he did for them.

There was one thing required of Tumba from day one, however, and that was to take part in the intense indoctrination of Islamic extremism. One of the most miserable parts of that training was participating in the five daily prayer sessions—such as right now.

Getting out of bed, Tumba slipped into his sandals and groped around in the dark till he found his water pitcher and rug. Then he hurried outside, joining the men who were washing themselves and arranging their rugs in rows in the dark courtyard. Several minutes later he was on his knees with the rest, chanting the prayers and going through the motions that he had memorized by now. However, in his heart, he prayed to God.

Lord, help me deceive these people, Tumba prayed within himself, even as his tongue recited meaningless words in Arabic. *You know that if they discover the real me, I am a dead man. And please forgive me again for denying you. I want to be faithful from now on.*

Every day he was troubled by the fact that he had renounced Christ. Every day he remembered Gambo and envied him. Every day he begged God for forgiveness. And every day he continued to play the dangerous game he was playing.

Every day the Boko Haram preacher and prayer leader in charge of Tumba was more convinced. Daily he watched Tumba and smiled at the fine young man who had converted to Islam. What he did not know was that Tumba was more convinced of Christianity every day, and that daily he prayed and watched for a chance to escape from his Sambisa prison.

It took eight months for Tumba's wrists to heal. And though they were left scarred and deformed, the pain was gone. He was delighted that he could use them almost as well as before.

No sooner had Tumba's wrists healed than Shadi, a captain in the Boko Haram army, started pressuring him to train as a warrior. "That's where we really need you," he explained. "We have lost a lot of our fighting men lately . . ."

"I am not cut out for fighting," Tumba answered quietly, stalling for time. "I can continue to do your errands. I am your slave to do whatever you want me to do."

What helped Tumba win this daily argument was that Shadi secretly liked him. Actually, everybody liked him. His quiet, friendly demeanor and his willingness to do any errand won the hearts of his captors. And that's how Tumba Tizhe became one of Boko Haram's favorite slaves for four long years.

In many ways life in the Sambisa Forest was good for Tumba. There was plenty of food because the Boko Haram warriors were constantly out raiding cities and towns. They always came back with their pickups loaded with all kinds of food. In spite of the apparent plenty, fear reigned, and Tumba knew it was hate that made Boko Haram tick.

During Tumba's four years in captivity, a big change came into his life when Abubakar arranged for him to marry a captive girl. Her Christian name was Laraba, but she was forced to convert to Islam and change her name to Zainab.

No one asked Tumba if he wanted to marry the girl they brought to him, a girl he did not know at all, but there seemed to be no other option. He was a slave, so he obeyed orders.

The marriage ceremony was short. He knelt on the rug beside the young woman, and when they asked him if he loved her, he answered "Yes." He knew it was the answer he was supposed to give. The emir then asked Laraba the same question, and of course she also said "Yes." That was it. Tumba and Laraba were married.

Tumba now had his own tent instead of living in a building with the other men captives. He continued to be an errand boy, and in many ways life was the same. But in another way, everything had changed.

Within a couple years two little daughters came to join him and his wife. First little Amira was born, and a year later Habuabtsa made her appearance. Though Tumba still felt young, he suddenly carried the responsibility of a father. He found out that Laraba had been a part of the EYN church, the same church he had attended, and he felt blessed because he got along well with her and loved his little girls.

It bothered Tumba that he was not able to raise his family in a godly manner. *There is no church here to be a part of,* he sighed sadly. *No pastors to give us instruction on marriage. No one to give us direction on how to raise our children or how to make a home work.*

Another major event took place about a year after Tumba was captured. It had been brewing for a long time, and it finally exploded. The two Boko Haram leaders, Abubakar Shekau and Al-Barnawi, had a fallout. They realized they could not both be the leader of Boko Haram, and they were too forceful and proud to work together.

Al-Barnawi was the son of Muhammed Yusuf, the founder of Boko Haram, who was killed in a clash with the Nigerian army in Maiduguri in 2009. Al-Barnawi struggled to become what his father had been in Boko Haram's beginning. But Abubakar was too strong and idealistic to be controlled by this "son of a wise man," the meaning of Al-Barnawi's full name.

Tumba was present when the two finally fought it out. After a fierce battle in which both sides lost many soldiers, they separated into two camps. During the fighting, things got so dangerous that Tumba took his family and fled into the forest, along with a number of others. They ended up in one of Al-Barnawi's encampments in the northern part of the Sambisa Forest.

Tumba rejoiced that during the conflict he was not forced to take up arms. After the dust settled, he continued being the handy errand boy in the new camp.

It was early. The sun had still not climbed high enough into the azure sky to start baking the habitants of the tree-sprinkled plains. From the door of their little mud hut, Tumba watched the activities in the plaza of the new village where he and Laraba now lived.

This time it was not Abubakar that directed the frenzy of activity. It was Al-Barnawi himself. He was the indisputable leader of the village, and his four hundred warriors chanted as they drilled, marched, and exercised. They practiced shooting—shooting to kill.

Tumba felt sad as he watched the young men, a lot of them even younger than himself. They were so dedicated to the Boko Haram cause. *What's so sad is how sincere they are. They actually think they are doing God a favor by being part of this insurrection. They think God is pleased with what they're doing. If only they knew the truth.*

As Tumba watched, staying back far enough in the hut so he would not be noticed, something else came to his mind. *If Gambo were here, he would boldly tell these boys about Jesus. He wouldn't be afraid to have them threaten to slaughter him. But I am afraid. I am not prepared to die. I am not bold enough to let them get a hint that I might still believe in Jesus.*

Confused and convicted, he again poured out his heart to God. "God, please forgive me! I am sure you have forgiven me for renouncing you, just as you forgave Peter for denying you."

After becoming part of Al-Barnawi's camp, life for Tumba changed little. He was still the willing errand boy. Just as in Abubakar's camp, the soldiers watched him closely at first, but it didn't take long to convince them that he did not need to be watched.

During the month of Ramadan, the Muslims fasted from sunup till sundown. Tumba and Laraba pretended to fast, but they ate on the sly whenever they could.

Hoping to further deceive his mentors, Tumba worked hard on getting his forehead callused. If a Muslim was able to create a dark spot on the center of his forehead, it proved that he prayed a lot. This was done by several methods, and Tumba tried them all.

Muslims pray with their faces to the ground. If they press down hard enough and long enough on their foreheads, they begin acquiring a callus. Many of the men, proud of their praying, would then stain their calluses by applying plant juices and even soot from their kitchen fires. They washed the dark patch off their foreheads soon after staining themselves so no one would notice it was artificial. With time and diligence, a permanent dark blotch could be acquired. Tumba tried all the tricks of the trade and acquired a conspicuous prayer blotch.

The weather was stifling hot. In the dry, bare yard Laraba was leaning over a fire, stirring rice that bubbled in a kettle perched on a tripod of stones. Sweat dribbled down her face and little Habuabtsa clung to her skirts.

"These hijabs[1] are so horribly hot!" Laraba complained, stopping to wipe her face with the billowing fabric that hung down over her shoulder. "Boko Haram is so strict about how women dress."

Tumba sat on a stump propped against the wall of the hut, holding Amira on his lap. "They sure are," he answered. "One of the things that is hard for me to understand is how Boko Haram can be right in some things and yet so wrong in others. It does not make sense."

Laraba added, "Some of their religion is from the Old Testament, but overall, their teaching is very different from what we believe in the EYN church."

Tumba nodded thoughtfully. "Has anyone ever explained to you what Boko Haram really means?" he asked.

Laraba shook her head.

"*Boko* means 'book,' " Tumba explained. "*Haram* means 'forbidden.' So what the name of this group of terrorists really means is 'books are forbidden.' "

"But why?" Laraba blurted out. "They have their own set of books, don't they?"

"That's right. They are not against all books. They have their own set of books they use and promote. It is books that promote western education that they despise. It's the influence from the West that Boko Haram rejects—all the modern stuff that is being brought in. And yes, some of what they stand for is good . . ."

During the four years in captivity under Boko Haram, Tumba had

---

[1] A *hijab* is a large, scarf-like piece of fabric that is draped over the head like a robe and usually reaches down to the feet. It only has a little window for the lady's face and is made from thin curtain-like material. It is the main way of knowing whether a lady is Muslim or not. To Boko Haram, being seen in public without it is a crime.

observed the Muslim extremists closely. He had taken note of several things Boko Haram stood for that were right.

"They hate abortion," he told his wife, shaking his head slowly. "That's good. They also teach their people to practice a high standard of modesty. In that they do better than some of the women in the EYN church."

Laraba nodded, stirring the rice for the last time. "They also hate the women's liberation movement . . . But then they treat their women like slaves. That's not right."

"But what they despise most of all, with a passion, is western education," Tumba added. "They don't allow musical instruments either."

"Supposedly they hate stealing," Laraba sighed. "Is it true that they cut off a robber's hand if they catch him?"

"I have never seen it done," Tumba answered, "but I've heard that it's true. I guess that's why hardly anyone steals. Again, it's so inconsistent. They might not steal *things,* but then they steal people like you and me. And, oh yes, they supposedly don't allow fornication or adultery, but they allow a man to have up to four wives. When he wants a new one, he just divorces the one he likes least and marries a younger one."

Laraba shook her head again.

"The Muslims believe in Allah," Tumba continued. "That's why they are constantly saying, *'Allahu Akbar.'* This phrase actually has a beautiful meaning: 'God is greatest.' But someone, somewhere, has perverted its meaning and it now means that Allah, the god of the Muslims, is the greatest. That change makes all the difference."

Laraba used an old rag to grab the edge of the cooking pot and lift the rice off the fire. She placed it on the ground to cool.

"That's our problem in Nigeria," Tumba said sadly. "We Nigerians are divided down the middle on this issue. You are either a Christian who knows that Jehovah is God, that Jesus is your Savior, and that the Bible is His Word, or you are a Muslim who thinks that Allah is God, that Muhammad was his prophet, and that the Koran is more important than the Bible."

"I feel sorry for the many captives who are slaves to Boko Haram," Laraba said with a sigh.

"We are slaves as well," Tumba added with a smile. "So I guess we can feel sorry for ourselves! I just wonder if this captivity will ever end."

Tumba and his little family were surrounded by captives all the time. And almost daily, the captives kept on coming—men, women, and children. If the men recanted, they were trained for jihad,[2] or if they were fortunate, they were made slaves like Tumba.

If the men wouldn't renounce Christ, they were slaughtered immediately. They were always led out of camp for the killings, but Tumba knew exactly what was happening.

The women were held as captives whether they renounced Christ or not, so most of the captives were women and children. And the women had it the toughest. The young girls sometimes ended up being concubines or were married off to the soldiers. The older women were forced to be slaves in a Boko Haram village.

The young boys were especially targeted by Boko Haram. They trained them for jihad and brainwashed them with Islamic extremism.

But despite all of Boko Haram's tactics, they were not able to brainwash Tumba. His determination to be faithful to God and to escape grew stronger every day. *Never again will I deny my Lord!* he vowed.

He was also determined to somehow escape with his family. Although it seemed hopeless at times, Tumba refused to give up. *My time will come!* he told himself.

---

[2] *Jihad* is a struggle or fight against the enemies of Islam.

Part four
The Time Comes

A stiff wind was rising, and the leaves on the abundant trees in the Sambisa Forest were kicking up their heels. An immense black cloud was billowing up over the northeastern horizon, and every inhabitant of the forest knew it was going to rain. But Tumba, straddling his bicycle, was not thinking about the upcoming rain.

Tumba stood as if cemented to the ground, watching the heart-wrenching scene. The Boko Haram soldiers were loading up a truckload of people. And among the victims was his own precious family. All he could do was wave at them, hoping they would see him. Tears blinded his eyes.

That morning, as usual, Tumba's slave drivers had him run an errand to a neighboring village. When he came back, pedaling his old jalopy bicycle under the hot sun, he was shocked to discover that what he had feared was now coming true.

"They are taking Laraba and my children!" Tumba moaned to himself. He felt like screaming, but he didn't dare open his mouth. Tumba knew better than to protest to his superiors. One wrong move could cost him his life. So he fled to his mud hut and wept.

After a good cry, Tumba prayed. "God, the time has come for me to escape. If my family is gone, I have no reason to stay. If I try to escape, I might get caught and killed. Or I might starve. But if I stay, I will starve anyway. And now I don't have my family. They are gone. O Lord, please help me escape!"

During the past several years, Tumba had taken every chance he got to speak to people and learn more about the area. It had become clear to him that escape was virtually impossible, especially with his wife and children. One reason was the tremendous distance involved in getting out of the Sambisa Forest. It would require days of walking to get from the camp where they were staying to a village that did not support Boko Haram. And even if they could handle the walking distance, they didn't know the way, and getting lost in the vast wilderness did not seem like a good option. They would likely die of thirst or be attacked by wild animals before they got to safety.

As time went on, the situation had become more critical. Because Boko Haram was being overpowered by the army and chased north again, there was suddenly not enough to eat. The warriors seldom went out on raids, so they didn't bring in food as they used to.

Tumba and his family realized they were slowly starving. Though they foraged far and near for edible tree leaves and tubers to make their soup, they were simply not getting enough to eat. The children suffered most, and it broke Tumba's heart to see it.

Even as the hundreds of slaves slowly starved, the bigshots usually had plenty to eat. As the situation got more desperate, Al-Barnawi began sending trucks to drop off women and children in distant villages where supposedly there was more food. Often he took them across the border into Niger or Chad where he knew the people could find refugee camps. Tumba constantly worried that the soldiers would take his wife and children.

Now it had happened. Tumba's heart was broken, but he was not surprised.

The next day Tumba pedaled his way toward one of the closest villages on yet another errand. A half mile up the road he stopped and picked up a bag with several pounds of mandioca flour and a jug of water that he had hidden in the bushes the night before. He tied everything securely to the back of his bike.

Once he arrived in town, he again watched for people to talk to. With a prayer in his heart, he pedaled his way through town, his errand completely forgotten. At the other end of town he noticed an old man walking down the road toward him. Tumba stopped his bicycle and waited until he got closer.

The man was a stranger, dressed like a poor farmer. His face was as wrinkled as a prune, but his eyes seemed kind.

Could this be my angel? Tumba wondered. *If ever I needed an angel, I do now.*

There was no one else in sight, so Tumba struck up a conversation with the old man. "I am from Michika," he began warily. "Where are you from?"

The old man seemed friendly and sincere, and it wasn't long till Tumba was pouring out his story. "I am escaping from Al-Barnawi," he confessed. "How can I escape? Where can I go?"

The old man looked around carefully. Then, lowering his voice, he pointed to the southwest. "If you walk in that direction, you will not run into any people or villages. Look for the town of Damboa. You should come to a highway that runs east and west. Once you get to the highway, you can ask which direction leads to Damboa. Once you are in Damboa, you are safe."

"How long will it take me?" Tumba asked. His mouth was dry and he could feel his heart pounding. *I need to hurry and get moving before somebody comes by.*

Shaking his head slowly, the old man answered, "It will take you almost two weeks. But it's your only option. If you go any other direction, you will get caught."

"Thanks!" Tumba croaked to the man, who was still taken aback by this sudden meeting. "Thank you so much!"

Tumba

Tumba quickly tied his water jug to his waist and unstrapped the bag of flour from his bicycle. Then, abandoning his bicycle, he started up the bank toward the southwest.

"You will meet the Fulani," the man called after him. "But don't be afraid of them. Be nice to them and they will be nice to you. They might even give you food."

Tumba barely heard. He was running toward the first stand of palm trees that lifted their bushy heads high, standing out starkly on the clay-red plain. *Once I get to the palm trees, no one can see me leave!* he told himself. He panted as he ran.

"May God go with him!" the old man muttered, wondering what he should do with the bicycle. Shaking his head, he watched Tumba disappear into the cluster of palms. "Slim chance he'll make it."

Then, grabbing the bicycle by a handlebar and rolling it alongside him, the old man shook his head again and muttered, "May God go with him!"

The morning dawned bright and clear. The tree-studded plain resembled some grand picture, framed for a rich person in a mansion. The trees, their branches slashed periodically to feed the Fulani's sheep and cattle, were squat and stubby. Their green, bushy tops stood out in stark contrast to the red dirt below.

Tumba stood behind a shrub oak tree, cautiously peering out like a coyote in hiding. He had stopped under the tree to eat the last of his mandioca flour mixed into a tasteless, sticky paste with water from his jug. He had seen a little Fulani village in the distance and had hopped behind the tree to hide. Though the Fulani didn't nearly all support Boko Haram, most of them were Muslims.

What shall I do? he wondered. *I've been traveling southwest for a week now. I still don't quite trust them, but I really do need food. They might be Boko Haram supporters and take me captive. I would be a worthy prize for their emir to give to Al-Barnawi for future favors.*

To Tumba, the week he had been walking had seemed like forever. Whenever he got tired, he found shade and slept on the ground. He kept his built-in compass accurate by watching the sun. Often he walked during the night because it was much cooler. Then he was guided by the moon and the stars.

Tumba was as stealthy as a fox. Never once did he allow himself to be seen. Even the Fulani herdsmen, who are often sharper than foxes, never got a glimpse of him. He always hid in the bush or skirted their camps.

But now he was out of food. His already skinny frame was thinning, and he could feel his strength waning. Something had to change, and soon! He desperately needed food. *Yes,* he finally decided, *I have to take the chance.*

Stepping out from behind the tree, Tumba walked toward the village, determination written all over his face. *The old man told me that if I am nice to the Fulani, they will be nice to me. Plus, the Sambisa Forest is many miles behind me.* He tried to inject courage into his system, but even as he walked, his legs felt wobbly.

Since it was still early, the herd of thirty cattle was milling around next to the camp, waiting till the herdsmen finished the milking and ate their meager breakfast. The cattle's dark red color and their long white horns stood out clearly on the plain. Just beyond the cows stood the little Fulani shacks, bustling with morning activity.

Tumba knew better than to walk up abruptly to the cow herd. He knew Fulani cattle were often skittish and would spook and run if he wasn't careful. Leaving ample distance as he skirted the herd, he approached the shacks cautiously. One of the men was milking the cows and noticed him. Setting down his bucket, he walked over to where Tumba stood under a bushy-headed tree.

After greeting each other in Hausa, Tumba stated his case: "I am running away from Boko Haram, from the Sambisa Forest," he began timidly. "And I need food. I have been walking for a week and I ran out . . ."

The Fulani farmer looked Tumba over. It was not hard to see that the fugitive's story was true. His clothes were dirty and tattered, his face was gaunt in hunger, and there was desperation in his eyes.

"Wait," the Fulani answered. He turned on his heels and strode back to their camp.

Tumba prayed under his breath. "God, please help me. I need you this morning. If these people capture me, I am sunk. If they don't give me food, I will starve."

The man went to one of the shacks first. When he came out, he carried a little bag and a bowl made from a split gourd. He stopped and dipped the bowl into his bucket of milk that waited patiently on a rock jutting out of the ground beside the cow herd.

Wordlessly, the Fulani handed Tumba the bowl of milk. Without answering, Tumba lifted the gourd to his lips. Then, tilting his head back, he drained it in one long draft. The look he gave the Fulani after he finished expressed his thanks. The Fulani smiled.

Next the Fulani gave the little bag to Tumba. As he took it, he returned the Fulani's smile. This time he did speak. "Thank you!" he said with feeling.

"You are welcome," the Fulani answered as he turned to head back to his shack.

It was evening when Tumba stopped trekking. The sun created long, spooky shadows as it dropped behind the trees.

Tumba flopped down between the protective buttresses of a huge baobab tree. Only then did he open the Fulani gift bag. There was a loaf of bread and several pounds of ground guinea corn. "Thank you, God!" he breathed as he sank his teeth into the bread. His mouth was too full and he was too weak to shout, but if he could have he would have said only one thing. "Thank you, Lord! This is the best food I have ever eaten!"

Tumba topped the knoll in long strides. Then he stopped, catching his breath as he tried to control his emotions. Down at the bottom of the hillside stood a little thatched shack made of clay. Tears welled up in his eyes.

He was home.

After two weeks of trekking, Tumba had come out onto the highway between Damboa and Biu. He had hitchhiked to Biu, then on to Uba. There he had a friend who took him on to Michika on his motorcycle. Except for his friend who drove the motorcycle, Tumba told no one who he was or where he was coming from. After they got to the village close to Michika where Tumba lived, the cycle driver returned home and Tumba walked back into the hills to his house. Now, at last, he had topped the last knoll and could see his house in the distance. Everything looked just as it had four years earlier.

Tumba's legs propelled him forward. Stumbling, blinded by tears, he fled down the hillside. As he approached the house, his mother, who was out behind the house sweeping the patio, saw him coming. Throwing up her hands and running to meet him, she cried, "My son! My son!"

After a warm embrace, both weeping, the two untangled as the rest of the six children crowded around. A half hour later the minister from Tumba's church arrived, as well as a dozen neighbors. Everyone wanted to hear his story. Bit by bit Tumba told them all that had happened to him in the four years he had been a captive.

Then the people around him saw his hands. The pastor grabbed them and held them up for all to see. Stroking the young man's scarred wrists, he croaked, "Tumba, what happened?"

His mother burst out crying again.

Tumba just stood there while all his friends and relatives touched or gazed at his scarred hands. Tears welled up in his eyes as he told them the story.

"How did you survive?" the minister asked, shaking his head in disbelief.

Tumba looked him in the face. "I don't really know," he answered. "I guess I just knew I could not let myself get discouraged. And I prayed every day. I am sure that helped me."

Tumba's minister and the neighbors tried to convince him to go to the city and tell the police. "They need the information you can provide so they can continue fighting Boko Haram," his minister explained.

But Tumba only hung his head, saying, "I don't want to talk to the police. I am just glad God saved me, and I want to enjoy my family and work the land like I used to. Maybe someday I can find my wife and children and they can join me."

"But the Boko Haram might come and kill you. You know they have their ways. They have supporters in almost all the villages. You know way too much about what's going on in the Sambisa Forest. Your life is in danger. If you told the authorities your story, the government would probably take you somewhere to protect you. They would help you get an education."

"God will take care of me," Tumba replied, shaking his head. "All I want to do is be at home, go to church, and work our land."

Once the community saw that Tumba would not waver, they gave up trying to get him to report his experiences to the police. Like him, they were just glad he was back home. They dropped the subject and returned to their own houses, thanking God that He had rescued another one of their people from the terrible grips of the Boko Haram.

That night Tumba dined on his favorite dish, draw soup prepared by his mother. He had a hard time falling asleep. He could hardly believe he was at home again, safe and sound. Tears welled up in his eyes again as he remembered his harrowing ordeal, especially the last two weeks of traveling alone through the wilderness. *I prayed to God every day, and He answered my prayers! Maybe someday He will help me find my wife and children. Thank you, Lord!*

Chapter 2

Under the Tamarind Tree

An indigo tint saturated the western sky and contrasted with the blackness of the vast sea underneath. The first stars twinkled courageously. The silence of the night was enhanced by the distant, gentle lapping of the waves on the ship's prow. The immense steamer plowing its way southward in the Atlantic seemed like a drop of dew on the surface of the ocean. So tiny in comparison. So insignificant. So vulnerable.

Stover Kulp leaned against the stern of the ship and stared at the melancholy scene. Though his eyes saw the beautiful picture, he was not thinking of lovely sunsets or the vastness of God's creation. At that moment, his heart was many miles behind him. The longing he felt for the person he had left weeping at the harbor had become a massive ache that seemed almost as big as the ocean itself.

Oh, Ruth, forgive me. His heart trembled slightly, his tongue tasting the salt in the air. He could feel tears creeping up under his eyelids, threatening to spill out onto his cheek. It wasn't because he didn't love Ruth, his dear wife of only sixteen months, that he had temporarily abandoned her. It was because of their shared love for Jesus that they were making this sacrifice. It was a call they both felt—a call that gripped their hearts with love for the African people.

Burning in the pocket of his vest was a letter that Stover read and reread. The letter proved that though Ruth would miss him, she was in full agreement with what he was doing. She had handed it to him at the moment of their parting. "You have always inspired me to live like Christ, dearest . . ." the letter read in part. "And I know I received a precious treasure when you came into my life. I gladly send you out on this great adventure in God's name. When I should feel sad, I feel a great joy that overflows me."[1]

That evening Stover wrote her a letter in reply: "I like to look at the stars and think that the same ones are shining over you. One can see why God is called our Heavenly Father. The heavens are so brooding and protecting. They seem to give a kindly shelter to all . . . I wonder if the waves that lift our ship go on and on until they beat against the banks of the Thames and tell you I love you. On the spray that flies past me into the clouds to descend on London in the fog and rain I send my love."

Albert Helser accompanied Stover. He had left his wife Lola in the United States when he and Stover crossed the Atlantic. Stover had taken Ruth with him to England, where she would study nursing in London while Stover and Albert traveled on to Nigeria to find the place God wanted them to start a mission outreach. With a burning passion for the African people and the backing of the Church of the Brethren, Stover and Albert did what few American Christians had done in Africa before this.

It was December 29, 1922, when the two new missionaries disembarked in the port city of Lagos, in southern Nigeria. There they met

---

[1] Mary Ann Moyer Kulp, *No Longer Strangers,* The Brethren Press, Eligen, IL, 1968.

with the lieutenant governor, who approved a new mission in the Biu area in northeast Nigeria, among the Bura tribe in Borno State.

From Lagos the two men traveled over six hundred miles by train to Jos. From Jos they headed northeast for many more miles in a truck with thirty African carriers, who were to carry part of their huge load into the interior of the Northeast. In total they had fifty boxes of equipment and eleven pieces of luggage. Halfway into their journey, after five flat tires and no spares within many miles, Stover and Albert were forced to abandon the truck. Using some of their precious money, they hired a government-run organization to help them move forward. To Stover's delight, the rest of the journey was to take place on horseback, with a train of thirty carriers trailing behind.

Eleven days later, Stover and Albert arrived at their destination—the village of Garkida. They moved into a grass hut and started building the first mission compound.

The two greenhorns who so valiantly tackled the new venture had prepared themselves for hardship. But to their surprise, it was even worse than they expected. During their first ten months in Garkida, it seemed as if hardship was all life dealt them. The heat was stifling, and the cultural differences and language barriers were a real problem. There was opposition from the Muslim emirs, and loneliness was always grabbing at their emotions. But by far the worst were the sicknesses that seemed to constantly plague them.

In spite of their many hardships, every Sunday morning Stover and Albert worshipped with whatever group they could assemble.

The first Sunday found them in Jos. The three attendees who joined the two missionaries in their first worship service were the three Nigerians they had hired to be their helpers.

Sheihu was an older man, a Muslim, who had a lot of experience in trekking and overseeing carriers.

John, a young man who spoke English, automatically became their interpreter. He also became their cook. John was raised Muslim, but he had drifted from Islam and was considering becoming a Christian.

Garba was a converted youth who had attended a mission school in Lagos and was taking instruction for baptism.

It was an oddly mixed group. But Stover claimed a verse in his Bible: "For where two or three are gathered together in my name, there am I in the midst of them."[2] He accepted that promise, and that first Sunday he taught out of the second chapter of Luke, with John interpreting the message into Hausa.

The next Sunday, the service was held in a small village out in the middle of nowhere. This time the congregation had grown. Sheihu, John, and Garba were there again, eager to hear what the missionaries had to share. But this time they were blessed with the presence of their thirty carriers.

On the outskirts of the village of Garkida stood a handsome tamarind tree surrounded by rocks of all shapes and sizes. On the third Sunday morning, the tree spread its wide branches over a unique congregation. Stover, Albert, Sheihu, John, and Garba were there, of course, as well as a dozen or so other villagers. They came in all ages and sizes and sat around on the many rocks that served as pews.

Not far from the tree's squat trunk, an unusual rock jutted out of the brown Garkida soil. It was as big around as a washtub and nearly flat on top. After the crowd was seated, Stover stood behind this natural pulpit with a big smile on his suntanned face. Setting his Bible down on the rock's top, he began, "Friends and brethren, you are all welcome to this open-air service . . ."

John interpreted.

"Even though we don't have a chapel yet," Stover beamed, "I am sure the God of heaven is here with us and hears us just as well as if we were

---

[2] Matthew 18:20.

in some grand cathedral."

The date was March 17, 1923.

For many months, until they were able to build a chapel, Nigeria's first Church of the Brethren congregation worshipped every Sunday under the tamarind tree. It wasn't long until the Garkida people proved that northeast Nigeria was ripe for the Gospel, and the size of the group that gathered under the tamarind tree swelled.

One missionary house was finished and another one underway when Albert got hit with yellow fever. After several months of struggling with the illness, the two men finally had to abandon the unfinished project in Garkida to seek medical help. They left their belongings locked in the finished house and abandoned Garkida with heavy hearts.

They decided to go back to Jos, which has a cooler climate, to try to nurse Albert back to health. While they were there, Lola Helser and Ruth Kulp arrived to join their husbands. For Stover and Ruth, this was heaven on earth. Though the hardships continued, Ruth took to African life like a fish to water. It was obvious to all that she loved it!

Soon after the ladies arrived, the four decided to return to Garkida. They opened a Church of the Brethren school with twenty-six boys in attendance. Soon it grew to over a hundred boys attending classes every day.

From the very beginning, Stover and Albert had dispensed medicine. In 1924, Dr. Burke and his wife arrived to take over the expanding medical work, and the foundations were laid to build a hospital.

On April 17, 1924, the Church of the Brethren celebrated their first love feast.

The hardships continued. Albert finally had to leave Africa due to poor health. Then Ruth became sick with a severe form of dysentery. Soon afterward Stover and Ruth's first baby, Stover Kulp Jr., was born, but he died twelve hours after birth.

Because of her weakened condition, Ruth failed to recover from the hard delivery, and later that same night she too passed away, leaving her beloved Africa for a better country. As she died, she quoted the twenty-third Psalm. One of the last things she gasped was, "Oh God, save the Bura people . . ."

Ruth was buried under a mahogany tree on a dismal hillside, her baby on her breast. Today a lonely stone marker in a small graveyard on a barren hilltop speaks her name.

Time moved on and Stover battled alone. After Albert and Lola left and Ruth passed away, others came to fill the gap. The Lord blessed the work and the congregation in Garkida continued to grow. The Church of the Brethren soon became well established in Garkida and then spread rapidly into other villages.

Stover had labored in Nigeria almost three years when he took his first furlough to the United States. By then the hospital was finished and Dr. Burke was even doing surgeries. The schools were growing and Stover himself was writing the textbooks in Bura, some of which were already in use by the time Stover left.

Stover spent a year in the United States and England. In 1926, during Stover's absence, the Church of the Brethren held their first baptism in Garkida, and four Nigerians were added to the church. During this time, Stover met and married Christina Masterton, who also had a life-long vision for mission work. At the end of the year he and his new wife returned to Nigeria where Christina, or Cris, as she preferred to be called, filled the gap that Ruth had left. The couple served as a team, just as Stover and Ruth had done before Ruth's untimely death.

Stover and Cris labored long and hard in northeast Nigeria. They saw God's blessing on their work as the church grew by leaps and bounds.

Twenty-nine years after Stover's feet touched African soil, his dear Cris also died of heart disease. They buried her on the hillside beside Ruth, where today another stone marker speaks her name.

Stover worked in northeast Nigeria for a total of forty years. In 1963 the mission board advised him to retire, and he returned to the United States. The Church of the Brethren in Nigeria had grown a lot more than Stover had ever dreamed. When he retired, there were forty congregations sprinkled throughout the Northeast, with a total membership of almost eighteen thousand.

In a place where education had been almost nonexistent, the Church of the Brethren had helped start more than forty schools, high schools, and colleges in many of the cities and villages where they had planted churches. Where there was hardly any help for sickness before, there were now two general hospitals and a leprosarium. By the time Stover retired, numerous Nigerian pastors served in the many congregations.

Stover left Africa for good in 1964 and died later that year at the ripe age of seventy. Thousands of black-skinned brethren in Nigeria and as many white-skinned Americans mourned his passing. They all knew, from both sides of the ocean, that by God's grace Stover had played a key role in the establishment of the Church of the Brethren in Nigeria.

In the East Coventry Mennonite cemetery south of Pottstown, Pennsylvania, there is a simple granite stone that carries a bronze plaque bearing this inscription:

H. STOVER KULP
1894-1964
Co-founder of the Church of the Brethren Mission in
Nigeria, West Africa, where he served from 1922-1963,
counting not the cost but committing his life to God in
service of his brethren.

The above story is only one story of how the Gospel got to Africa. Many other Christian churches have flourished all over Africa.

It seems too bad that in some parts of Africa, including northeast Nigeria, Islam took root before Christianity did. We may never fully understand God's timing, but in His time, He raised up a people for Himself. In a hostile land where Jesus was hated, many churches and thousands of Christians were bold for Christ, including the EYN church which Tumba, Yakubu, and Gambo attended before their capture. The church flourished even though it often seemed as if Christianity and Islam could not exist in the same place at the same time. Nigeria seemed not to have room for both.

But God has a purpose. Even today, while fifty percent of Nigeria's population adheres to Islam and fifty percent professes Christianity, God's arm is not shortened to save. God is speaking to Muslims in many ways, especially through dreams and visions. God loves them, even as He does you and me. As a result, many Muslims are turning to God Almighty.

Boko Haram did not take God by surprise. He was watching the dramatic scene from His throne in heaven. He watched it develop. He knew that the followers of Boko Haram were an angry, bitter people who needed Jesus. Their religion knew no grace. No peace.

In His love and mercy, God Almighty prepared Himself a people who would show love in the face of extreme hate. Though it cost the blood of many martyrs, God has used the church to give these terrorists a touch of His love. The genuine Christian's testimony is what God uses to speak the loudest to the followers of Allah.

The Boko Haram soldiers were amazed when they saw thousands of Christians who refused to fight back. They were stunned when they saw hundreds of these spiritually courageous people turn around and love their enemies, blessing them and praying for them. But what really shook them to the core were the hundreds of fearless Christians who chose to die rather than renounce the Jesus they loved. The testimonies shared in this book are just a few examples of God's work in northeast Nigeria.

Chapter 3

The Dazzling Curtain

Ishaku Muhamad, a converted Muslim, stared at the delightful scene, goosebumps popping up all over his body.

Angels! Hundreds of them—dressed in pure white. It was as if they were standing to attention in a wide circle surrounding him.

Between Ishaku and the angels were dozens of little children, also dressed in white. They danced in a circle around Ishaku, singing songs of praise.

The angels and the children were praising God. The music was so beautiful that it almost made Ishaku cry, and he was not one to cry easily. He rejoiced in his heart. *This is truly the music of heaven!*

To one side of the splendid scene there hung an immense curtain, also dazzling white, and edged with gold that glittered. Ishaku longed to approach the curtain, to look behind it, to discover what lay beyond. But in his heart he knew he couldn't go near without permission. It was much too magnificent.

Ishaku looked down and realized that he too was dressed in shining white.

Actually, everything in the whole area was shining. The brightness gave him the impression that he was standing in the very presence of God.

Suddenly the music stopped, and Ishaku swung to face one of the angels. "Ishaku," the angel said in a voice that sounded like music. "You have been a hot-tempered man . . ."

Ishaku hung his head in shame. He nodded, acknowledging the truth.

"You need to change that. You need to be humble and meek."

Again Ishaku nodded, incapable of uttering a word. He just knew that he would change. He desired it so much.

The angel continued speaking now, looking straight at Ishaku. "The Mighty One is coming to meet you . . ."

Immediately Ishaku heard music coming from behind the curtain. Soft. Rousing. Beautiful. Even the angels and the children were silent now, their faces bright with anticipation. Ishaku trembled in expectation.

The curtain stirred. An immense Being came out from behind the curtain and took a seat close to Ishaku on what might have been a throne, right in the center of the scene. The Being was beyond description—too vast, too bright, and too glorious.

A strange luminous radiance enshrouded everything, blocking out the Being's true form. He was just there. Extremely present. Totally beautiful. Overwhelmingly glorious. Terrible and yet full of love. Ishaku found himself lying flat upon his face before the Being.

Then a voice, like the sound of many waters, said, "Ishaku, if you follow me, I will bring you to this place and you will live here with me forever."

Even from the ground, which was also as white as snow, Ishaku could see the Being that filled everything. He shivered in fear and delight when the Being stretched out his hand and touched him on his side.

Suddenly Ishaku woke up, overwhelmed and weeping with joy.

He sat up in his bed, waking his wife Rebeca. "What's wrong, love? What happened?" she cried, reaching for her flashlight.

Rebeca was surprised to see her husband sitting on the bed weeping.

"What happened, Ishaku?" she asked again.

The noise woke little Damaris, the one-year-old baby that slept between them in their bed. Rebeca quickly picked her up and rocked her as they talked.

The dream came out, bit by bit. Rebeca could see it had left a tremendous impact upon her husband. He told her the story, first as if in awe. Then, as he narrated, he got more and more excited.

"The Mighty One was God!" Rebeca exclaimed, once the story had been told. "This is awesome!"

"It was Jesus!" Ishaku echoed, still weak from the experience. "He loves me so much!"

"The Mighty One actually spoke to you!" Rebeca whispered, stroking Damaris's hair. "And the angel did as well. You know I have talked to you many times about your temper, Ishaku. Now I believe you will change."

Ishaku nodded, drying his tears.

"Do you know who the children were?" Rebeca asked. "Probably they are your Sunday school children. Someday you will be in heaven with them . . ."

Ishaku nodded, tears welling up again. He remembered his Sunday school class and how he enjoyed teaching them.

Then a more serious thought arose in his mind. "Rebeca, do you think this dream means I am going to die?"

"It could be a warning," Rebeca agreed soberly, giving little Damaris a kiss on her forehead. "It means we should always be prepared, that's for sure. And praise the Lord He showed you what you need to work on."

"I am not afraid to die!" Ishaku exclaimed, reaching over and squeezing his wife's hand. "If I die, I will go to that beautiful place. Oh Rebeca, how I wish I could describe that wonderful place to you."

Life went on for Ishaku, Rebeca, and Damaris in their home city of Potiskum. They couldn't forget the dream, but they no longer had the feeling that Ishaku would die soon. The dream was a gift, apparently, and not a warning. Although all of northeast Nigeria was in a stir because of what the Boko Haram terrorists were doing in the nearby city of Damaturu and other areas, Rebeca and Ishaku did not sense danger in their own city.

One day, about a month after Ishaku had the dream, the family went a short distance to another neighborhood of Potiskum to visit Ishaku's oldest sister. During their visit they began discussing the Boko Haram activity in Damaturu.

"It all started so innocently," Ishaku explained to the group. "Men dressed in white began to meet in one of the parks. There they taught the youth about Allah. I remember when I was taught like that, years ago, by a Muslim teacher."

"I am so glad you were converted to Christ, though," Rebeca beamed, "because if not, I would never have married you."

"Yes," Ishaku's sister remembered. "Those men dressed in white made it look as if they were bringing a revival to the Islamic religion. So many Muslim youth fell for the trap. It is so sad."

"The military finally saw what was happening. They quickly tried to clamp down on the group, but they fought back like tigers. Quite a few people were killed during that first confrontation."

"The same thing happened in Maiduguri," Rebeca reminded the group. "A lot of people on both sides were killed there. In the hundreds, they say . . ."

"It's those left over who are wreaking havoc on the whole Northeast," Ishaku sighed. "It's so sad that we Nigerians have to suffer because of some radicals who don't fear the true God."

Toward evening, when Ishaku was outside talking with his sister's husband, Rebeca heard what sounded like gunfire in the distance. She rushed outside to her husband and exclaimed, "That sounds like gunfire! I am afraid!"

Ishaku shook his head, then chuckled, "You are too easily frightened. It's probably some birthday party, and they are setting off fireworks."

"The gunshots came from the direction of our neighborhood," Rebeca insisted, a frown on her forehead. "You can stay if you want to, but I am going home."

"I'll come later," Ishaku answered, still smiling. "See you soon."

The sun dropped down over the horizon and the shadows jumped out at every street corner as Rebeca clung to Damaris and walked rapidly down the street. *Boko Haram has never come to our city before,* she consoled herself as her feet sped along. *But then again, a person never knows when the first time will be.*

As Rebeca approached their house, she remembered Ishaku's dream. Fear clutched anew at her heart. She could see the roof of their humble abode protruding out over their courtyard wall. She knew nobody was at home. Or was there? Suddenly she was afraid to enter the house by herself.

Then Rebeca heard gunshots again, much closer than before. Quickly she headed toward her neighbor's house, seeking protection.

Mega, their next-door neighbor, had also converted from Islam to Christianity. He was an older man of some means, and Rebeca knew his commitment to Christ was as genuine as sterling silver. She opened the gate of Mega's courtyard and sprinted toward his house, feeling a foreboding sense of urgency. He met her at the door, a cloud hovering over his usually friendly face.

"This sounds bad!" Mega murmured as he pulled Rebeca into the house, closing the door behind her. "There is no way to know what all is going on. God will be with us."

Rebeca felt relieved once she was in the house. "Now we should be safe," she whispered to the baby she carried in her arms.

"Where is your husband?" Mega wondered, offering Rebeca a seat. Mega's wife, Kate, and his mother, Sonia, joined them.

Rebeca explained Ishaku's absence. Then she asked, "Do you think it's Boko Haram?"

Their conversation was interrupted by the grating sound of Ishaku and Rebeca's gate in the adjacent courtyard, opening and closing again. "That's probably my husband," Rebeca whispered, looking out the windows of Mega's house, which were still open. "Maybe I should run over."

At that moment two youths burst into Mega's courtyard from the street and rushed into the house. Rebeca immediately recognized them as Koji and Cristofer, two local Christian youths who attended the same church she and Ishaku did.

"It's the Boko Haram!" they hissed. Fear shone in the two boys' eyes.

Mega locked the courtyard gate and closed all the doors and windows. "It's time to lie low," he announced, trying to keep his cool. "This sounds bad!"

An hour and a half passed. Holed up in Mega's house, the group of believers heard three gunshots over in Ishaku's compound. Rebeca covered her face with her hands. "They shot my husband," she sobbed. "I guess his dream is coming true . . ."

"It's time to pray," Mega announced desperately. "Let's all kneel here in a circle."

It was a solemn group that knelt together in Mega's living room that evening, but not all of them were ready to die.

Sonia, Mega's mom, was a devout Muslim. Though she loved her son and respected his beliefs, her ears had always been deaf to God's will for her life. How many times had her son witnessed to her and she had refused to listen? She had always been afraid that someday Mega would fall into the hands of Boko Haram. Now all she could do was weep as Mega prayed his heart out for them all.

Rebeca and Kate were prepared to die, so they prayed along with Mega and were comforted. But the cry of their hearts still remained, *What will happen this terrible night?*

"What do you smell?" Rebeca asked a while later. "It smells like smoke!"

"They're burning down your house!" Mega gasped, rushing to the back door of the house. "I'm afraid the fire will jump across the wall and burn ours too."

Though Sonia and Kate protested, Mega now opened the back door and slipped out into the courtyard. He sprinted across the courtyard and peeped over the low courtyard wall into Ishaku's compound. Not only did he see the flames that were starting to eat up the house, but he found himself looking up the barrel of an AK-47 rifle.

"Open your front gate," the soldier barked, holding the bead on Mega's forehead. "And no tricks!"

"I won't play any tricks," Mega assured the angry man kindly. "I will cooperate."

Mega burst into the house, panting. "They saw me!" he hissed. "I have to open. Ladies, go hide in the bedroom! All of you!"

Minutes later two soldiers burst into the house and began ransacking it. Finding the folks cowering in the bedroom, they herded them out into the courtyard. "Get down on your faces!" one soldier barked. Without hesitation, the women and the two youths, Koji and Cristofer, joined Mega, who was already in a prone position.

After the soldiers had discussed the situation in whispers, they suddenly changed their orders. "Women, go back into the house!"

Once they got to the bedroom again, Kate came up with an idea. She opened a dresser drawer and took out something, then quickly slipped outside into the darkness. Rebeca followed at a distance, watching.

Kate approached the Boko Haram soldiers boldly, and then respectfully said, "I am giving you a gift. God bless you."

With a look of surprise, the soldier accepted the wad of cash. *Will this touch of love soften these hard men's hearts?* Rebeca wondered, fear still filling her ripped-up heart.

The soldiers counted the money greedily: ten thousand naira.[1] Then they waved the two women back into the house. Retreating, but still close enough to hear, they heard the Boko Haram leader throw the terrible question at the three men, "Are you Christians?"

The women fled for the bedroom before they heard the answer.

As the soldiers' guns spoke three times, the women fell to their knees.

---

[1] Nigerian currency amounting to about US$28.

They knew the truth. Even Sonia was praying to Jehovah now. If it was Allah who was telling Boko Haram to kill her son whom she loved so much, then all that was left to do was cry out to her son's God.[2]

The rest of the night was pure terror for the three women. First, the soldiers came and forced them to step outside to see the three bodies lying on the ground in pools of their own blood. Then the angry men raved and ranted, cursing any religion that wasn't Islam. "Anyone who is not a Muslim is an infidel!" the leader snarled. "And we must kill them." Kicking his foot against Mega's inert body, he continued, "This man used to be a Muslim, but then he turned into a traitor. These two young men also claimed they were Christians, so they had to die. Allah is the only true God."

The terrorists commanded Rebeca and Sonia to go back into the house. Rushing into Rebeca's bedroom, the two women fell on their knees, as the baby slept on. There the two women spent the next several hours praying, weeping, and wondering what evil the men were doing to Kate.

It was after midnight when Kate returned. Brokenhearted, she poured out her awful story. "First they tried to make me take them to Christian homes so they could raid them. I refused. So they forced me to take them to Christian church houses."

"Oh my!" Rebeca gasped. "What did you do?"

"I led them to two church houses," Kate admitted. "They burned the Catholic Saint Paul's to the ground. And they destroyed our ECWA chapel by placing a bomb in it. After the explosion, they burned what was left. They finally released me and left."

As night gave way to dawn, the three women were finally convinced that the terrorists had left. They decided to leave the house to look for help. Rebeca picked up her innocent little baby, and they cautiously started out. As they tiptoed through the courtyard, they walked past the lifeless bodies of Mega, Koji, and Cristofer. It was almost more than Rebeca could handle.

---

[2] Soon after this, Sonia publicly announced that she was converted, saying, "I want to go where Mega is!" Weeks after her conversion, she became ill and God took her home to join Mega in eternal rest.

She was afraid she would faint.

Once out on the street, Sonia and Kate decided to head into the city to look for an ambulance. "Maybe if we can get Mega to the hospital we can still save his life," Sonia kept repeating.

Rebeca shook her head in disbelief, clutching her little girl. *She saw his dead body and she still thinks they can save him!*

Fearing the worst, Rebeca decided to go see what had happened in their own compound. As she approached the gate to their courtyard, she could see the roof of their house, which protruded above the wall. It was black from the fire that had gutted their home.

Rebeca was surprised to see her twelve-year-old sister, Beatrice, and another lady come running out of the next house down the street. "Rebeca," Beatrice cried, her face pale and distraught, "they killed Ishaku last night!"

Rebeca took her into her arms and answered, "Yes, I heard the gunshots and figured that's what happened. But let's go see."

The gate to the courtyard was open. The ladies stepped inside. Rebeca thought she was ready for anything, but to see the lifeless body of her husband and two of his friends stretched out on the ground in front of the charred house was overwhelming. Steeling herself, she stepped closer to her husband's body. The other two bodies lying there beside Ishaku were also those of former Muslims. One was Mohamad, a good friend of Ishaku, and the other was Markus, a young man who had recently converted from Islam to Christ. Mohamad's wife, Susanne, stood beside Rebeca, sobbing into her hands.

Seeing the mangled bodies of her husband and his friends struck a chord deep within Rebeca's heart. Hugging her baby to her breast, she cried and cried. Beatrice clung to her and cried along with her older sister.

Finally Rebeca got control of her emotions and, wiping her eyes, she whispered to Susanne and Beatrice, "All three of these men were prepared to die. It's no wonder Boko Haram targeted these two compounds. Four of the men who died last night were former Muslims who converted to

Christianity, and the soldiers somehow knew it. It makes them so angry when their own people renounce their faith to accept Christ."

"They think they gained a great victory by killing them," Susanne sighed, wiping the tears from her eyes. "But they are so wrong! The victory was won by those who died. They are now safe in the arms of Jesus."

Rebeca refused to enter her charred house. She turned and led her friends out of the compound and on toward their church where she would find her minister. She needed help to know what to do with the bodies, and she needed comfort from her church family. She also needed a place to rest and to somehow try to make sense out of her life that had suddenly been turned upside down.

As the trio walked toward the church, Beatrice and Susanne told Rebeca the story of their horrible night.

The evening before, after Ishaku and Beatrice had come home, their friend Mohamad and his wife Susanne, as well as Markus, had stopped by as they often did. They had all been nervous because of the shooting they could hear in the distance.

The little group had sat in the living room, anxiously talking in low tones. Ishaku wondered why Rebeca hadn't come home, and by 8:30 the atmosphere in the living room was extremely tense. Suddenly two Boko Haram soldiers, clutching AK-47s, strode into the room as if it were their own home. The little group of Christians was shocked.

"Give me your money!" was the first thing the Boko Haram leader demanded.

The three men produced what little money they had, after which the soldiers ushered them out into the dark night. Beatrice and Susanne trembled in the living room, praying in their hearts. After that, the ladies couldn't see the events unfold, yet the story was seared into their minds because they had heard everything clearly.

"Get down on your faces," one of the terrorists had barked.

Beatrice could imagine Ishaku obeying quickly. That's the way he was.

He would be nice to the wicked men all along, not resisting but accepting their commands. Ever since his dream, Ishaku had been a different man.

The suspense in the living room was intense. The ladies could only imagine what it felt like to be out in that dark courtyard, facedown, with the Boko Haram terrorists cursing you. Then they heard muffled, angry voices out in the dark.

Suddenly a loud and clear question rang out into the night, "Are you a Christian?"

The answer, equally loud and clear, echoed back. "Yes."

There was silence for a moment.

Oh, what a battle was raging in the spiritual world!

Then again, "Are you a Christian?"

"Yes, I am!"

Silence.

One last time, "Are you a Christian?"

Swiftly the reply came, "Yes!"

Silence.

The ladies cringed when what they expected actually happened.

Boom!

Was that Ishaku?

Boom!

That's probably Mohamad.

Boom!

Could that be Markus?

After the massacre, the soldiers entered the house and ordered Susanne and Beatrice to the next house down the street. Then they lit up Ishaku's house.

Once the ladies got to their neighbor's house, they were shocked to see that the soldiers had already done their dirty deeds there as well. They had shot the man of the house, but not fatally, and the family had rushed him to the hospital. In the wee hours of the morning, they got the news that the man had died.

Now, as the three women approached the pastor's house, right next to the chapel, they saw that everything was chaos. The chapel had been burned down, and the pastor, they learned, had fled during the night but was now back. He and about a dozen other church leaders and members were busy figuring out where to start restoring order.

For a while Rebeca wasn't even able to talk to her pastor because of all the people milling around, also needing help. Meanwhile, the army had picked up the bodies and taken them to the morgue at the hospital. Later the church rallied around the widows and family members of those who had been killed, seeing to it that the men received a proper burial.

A lovely picture came to Rebeca many times during the next two days while she and her friends mourned and dealt with their shock. And every time she would whisper, "Thank you, thank you, Jesus, for Ishaku's dream!"

In her mind, Rebeca would see Ishaku as he walked up to the dazzling curtain. He was surrounded by children and angels singing praises to God, and was dressed in clothes as white as the curtain itself. She had to catch her breath every time when she thought how lovely the music must have been.

Ishaku's dream had ended before he entered his reward. But in her imagination, Rebeca often continued the vision beyond that point. It encouraged her as she pictured the Mighty One being there to welcome His servant home.

In her reverie she would picture the Mighty One opening wide His arms to welcome her husband. "Well done, my good and faithful servant!" He would exclaim. "Welcome home to your eternal rest!"

At the end of her daydream, Rebeca would whisper words that the Mighty One loved to hear. Words that spurred her on to follow Him until the end. "I will follow you, O Mighty One, like my husband did. Help me be faithful till the end."

And then, with her eyes glistening, she would add, "I am coming, my dear Ishaku. I am coming soon!"

Chapter 4

Chibok Girls

Part one

Moonlight Leap

An eerie half-moon peered through the scattering of clouds that hung low in the sky over the spacious buildings of the Government Girls' Secondary School (GGSS) in Chibok, Borno State, in northeastern Nigeria. The moon had no way of knowing what was developing that awful night of April 14, 2014. But the Heavenly Father knew, and He watched over the 270 high school girls who slept soundly in their cozy beds in the school's bunkrooms.

The time was 11 p.m.

Seventeen-year-old Salomi, fast asleep in her bunk, was awakened suddenly by volley after volley of gunshots in the distance. Sitting up in her bed, she clutched her heart with her hands. *That sounds like war! Could it be the infamous Boko Haram?*

Salomi didn't wait for the answer. In a second she was out of bed, dressing faster than she had ever dressed before. *If it's Boko Haram, we have to be ready. Lord, help us!*

All through the bunkhouse the 270 schoolgirls, most between the ages of sixteen and eighteen, dressed as fast as they could. They had all realized the danger they faced in returning to school. Several months earlier, because of the atrocities Boko Haram fighters were inflicting on Christians in the Northeast, GGSS had closed down. But during a lull in the storm, the students had been called in again for several days to take the final tests for the year.

The gunshots didn't die down. The noise came from the village of Chibok, which lay just beyond the high school's courtyard. In terror, the girls wondered what was happening in the village. What they didn't know was that the guards responsible for protecting the school had already run for the bush.

Salomi was fully dressed by then, and Margaret, one of her roommates, snapped on the lights. "Wh-what's going on?" Margaret stammered. But in the hearts of all the girls, they knew all too well what the most likely explanation was.

Whispering among themselves, their teeth chattering, the girls shivered in fear. One hundred unanswered questions flew from heart to heart as the girls waited. Suddenly a soldier strode into their bunkroom and raised his hand. "Look, don't panic. There is trouble in the village." The tall soldier spoke in their common Hausa language. "We have come to protect you. Follow me."

The girls stared at the soldier, not convinced that he was a trustworthy protector. But all they could do was obey, so they followed him out into the large dining area. As they exited the room, Salomi clung to Margaret's arm. "What will happen to us?" she whimpered.

Margaret, ever the strong, composed girl in her dorm, answered, "We must trust in God, Salomi. That's all we can do."

To their surprise, all the girls from the whole bunkhouse were gathering in the dining room, escorted in by a dozen soldiers who did not look as if they were part of any organized army.

Salomi looked at the guard who had escorted her and her companions. His eyes were skittish, and Salomi could sense his fear. He had a straggly, unkempt beard. His clothes were old soldier fatigues that hadn't been washed in days. His boots were caked with dry mud and dust. *These are not soldiers from the Nigerian army,* Salomi realized. *This has to be the Boko Haram!* The fear printed on all the girls' faces told Salomi that the rest of her classmates suspected the same thing she did. They were being rounded up by the terrible Boko Haram.

As Salomi crouched in a corner, she noticed her close friend Yagana standing against the opposite wall of the dining hall, chewing her fingernails. Yagana was a short, chubby girl who was outgoing and talkative. Beside her stood Rifkatu, the tall girl who had the fame of being the prettiest girl in the school. Though she didn't show her fear as much as Yagana, her lovely face, as if set in stone, was much paler than usual.

Once all the girls were packed into the dining hall, the soldiers, all standing guard by the two exit doors, started chanting, *"Allahu Akbar! Allahu Akbar! Allahu Akbar!"*

No sooner had the men started chanting than a lot of the girls started crying. Not one girl said a word, not even Margaret, the brave one. Although she wasn't crying, Margaret hid her face in her hands, and Salomi knew she was praying.

"Our day has come!" Salomi sobbed. "Oh, Lord, please have mercy on us!"

After their chant, a tall soldier, who was obviously the leader, pointed at Yagana and barked, "Come with me and show me where the kitchen is."

Most of the soldiers followed the leader. Several soldiers stayed, guarding the doors.

During the next twenty minutes the soldiers looted the kitchen, taking the pots and pans and all the food, cooked or raw. They also ransacked the bunkrooms, taking anything they wanted. Then the soldiers returned and ordered the girls to follow them to the wide playground, a short distance from the buildings.

The gunshots had stopped. The girls were shocked to see blood red skies hanging over the village of Chibok. This could only mean one thing: they were burning houses in town. But nothing prepared them for what started happening next.

The soldiers created tall piles of stacked plastic chairs. Then they doused gasoline onto the stacks and lit them up. The fire ate up the chairs rapidly. As they were consumed, they served as torches for the wooden part of the roofs of the building. By the time the girls were being marched away, every single building in the high school complex was on fire—the chapel, the kitchen, the offices, the bunkrooms, and the school. They also burned several vehicles parked outside the high school building.

Never had Salomi been so afraid as when she saw them burn their school and heard the wicked men yell, *"Allahu Akbar! Allahu Akbar! Allahu Akbar!"* As the soldiers yelled their raucous cries, the hearts of the Chibok girls screamed for help. But there was no help for them that night.

"March!" the Boko Haram leader barked. "Line up and follow my men!"

The girls obeyed. Single file. And for once everything was quiet. Even the soldiers, walking among the girls, were quiet now. The girls didn't dare say a word, even to each other. They could hear only the rustle of their feet in the sand as they marched north toward the infamous Sambisa Forest. All the girls could do was weep, and weep they did! The waning moon looked down on the sad sight, and if the moon could shed tears, it would have wept along with them.

But beyond the moon, the all-knowing and loving Father was carefully watching as well. And if Jesus wept for the people in front of Lazarus' tomb two thousand years ago, He must have wept that night for the 270 girls whose hearts were being broken before the real nightmare had even begun.

After marching for miles, the girls arrived at a place where several large army trucks were parked beside the road. Another set of soldiers waited for them there. Their hearts chilled when the leader barked, "All of you crawl onto the trucks, and don't try any tricks or we will shoot you!"

Minutes later they were all crammed in three trucks. Salomi was sad that she did not manage to get on the same truck as her friend Margaret, but through the gloom she noticed that Yagana had ended up in the truck with her. All Salomi could do was hang on to her companions as the trucks started up, then lurched away into the dark night, plowing their way north.

Salomi tried to pray as she huddled among dozens of whimpering girls, but her mind was thinking of too many scary things to pray. *I wonder what Mother would say if she could see me here with the other girls, being hauled like cattle to these wicked men's camp. Will I ever see my mother again? What will happen to us now? These wicked men must have terrible plans for us. Lord, have mercy on us. Please!*

The truck wasn't roaring down the rough road long when Salomi noticed several things. First, there were no soldiers in the back of the truck with them. Second, she saw the girls dropping things onto the road so the townsfolk could easily follow their tracks—a headpiece, a handkerchief, a book, or whatever else the girls happened to have with them. Suddenly Salomi saw a girl jump off the back of the truck.

After another girl jumped off the side of the truck, Salomi felt a surge of courage. *If they can do that, I can too. Since we are the last truck in the escort, they might not catch me.*

Even as Salomi pushed her way toward the back of the truck, she realized that if the Boko Haram soldiers caught her, they would beat her and maybe even kill her. She deliberated. *But nothing could be worse than living in the Sambisa Forest with these wicked men.* She closed her eyes and took the plunge.[1]

---

[1] Nine girls jumped from the trucks that night, and they all escaped. The rest of the girls were afraid to jump.

Salomi landed in the sand and rolled. As soon as she landed, she realized that though she was bruised, she did not have any broken bones. Even as the truck whipped around a corner in the scant moonlight, Salomi was up and running.

Providentially, there was a small adobe shack beside the road. The door stood open. Forcing herself not to be afraid, Salomi burst into the front room. In the dim moonlight she saw that the hut was an old one and was not in use. She quickly pulled the dilapidated door shut behind her, then sprinted to a back room, to the farthest corner, and sat down in the dust.

"Thank you, thank you, God!" she whispered, even as she rubbed her bruised ankle. "I made it! O Lord, don't let a Boko Haram soldier find me. Please! In Jesus' name. Amen!"

It's probably 1 a.m., Salomi guessed. She held perfectly still, listening for any unusual sounds. All she heard was the piercing trill of the crickets and the occasional cry of a night bird. But try as she might, she could not sleep.

As the long hours until dawn ticked by, Salomi waited, prayed, and cried. Though she had escaped from the truck, some Boko Haram soldiers might still be around. During the night she heard footsteps go by several times, and twice a motorcycle zoomed past. But just as Salomi hoped, nobody stopped to check the abandoned hovel by the roadside.

When Salomi heard the first birds sing in the tree outside the shack, she knew the time had come to complete her escape. She straightened out her cramped body and carefully opened the door. The sun was not up yet and light was scarce. *But it is light enough to see, and I might as well make a run for it!*

Salomi looked up and down the road. "Praise the Lord, it's empty!" she cheered. Running as fast as possible, she started back toward Chibok, trembling from head to toe and watching every shadow.

Suddenly she heard the sound of motorcycles coming toward her from

Chibok. She froze, ready to run for the bushes, but it was too late. A whole row of motorcycles roared up and stopped. Salomi was relieved to see that they were young men from Chibok, some carrying guns. They were following the tracks of the trucks that had taken the girls.

The group of young men asked Salomi for her story. She filled them in briefly. Then they told her what they knew. In town, the Boko Haram had burned down the EYN chapel and had looted and burned several businesses and about a dozen houses belonging to Christians. "At least two other girls also jumped off the trucks," the young men told Salomi. "Those two came into the village in the wee hours of the morning. You are the third. Jump on one of the cycles and one of the boys will run you back to the village so you will be safe. The rest of us will follow the tracks to see if we can catch up with them."

Minutes later, as the sun burst over the horizon, Salomi saw the smoking remains of their beloved school as they drove past. Her heart was sad when she saw that everything was destroyed. Memories of the wonderful time she had spent there with her companions haunted her as they drove on into Chibok.

As they drove up to the town's square, tears flooded her eyes. A whole crowd of Chibok people were waiting for her. The first one to run out to receive her with a big hug was Yagana.

"Yagana, you escaped as well?" Salomi gasped, taking her bosom friend by the arms and looking her over.

"I sure did!" Yagana exclaimed. "I was the first one to jump. So you jumped as well?"

"I was the third one," Salomi sighed, hugging her friend again. "I saw someone jumping but didn't know who it was. It must have been you. Because of your courage I dared to jump. And praise the Lord, we are safe!"

The townspeople welcomed Salomi with open arms. Especially her parents wept with joy. The crowd asked Salomi many questions, and just like the other two escapees, she told and retold her story. But all the time her heart felt heavy and sad. *What will happen with my friends?*

Why me? Why Yagana? The question haunted Salomi. *Why were Yagana and I saved when over two hundred others are somewhere in that horrid Sambisa Forest under the wicked power of evil Boko Haram terrorists? How is Margaret? What happened to Rifkatu? Oh, how I worry for those precious girls!*

"Thank you, God!" Salomi prayed through her tears. "You saved me and now I want to serve you my whole life. Please watch over the other girls who are in the hands of the enemy. I am sure you can take care of them just as well as you took care of me."

Part two
Daughters of the King

The two young girls clung to each other in the darkness. Their bed was an old Muslim prayer rug spread out on the hard dirt floor of an abandoned house in the forest. Their soiled clothes reeked, and their hair was unkempt and dirty. "Rifkatu, are you okay?" Margaret whispered, still holding on to her best friend. "I can't sleep."

"I can't either," Rifkatu whimpered, snuggling closer to her friend. "I am afraid."

"I am afraid as well," Margaret confessed. "Very afraid. But mostly I am afraid for you."

Margaret allowed her hand to find Rifkatu's face in the darkness, and her fingers traced the beautiful features she knew so well. "You are so beautiful!" Margaret fussed. "Every Boko Haram commander will want you."

"But you are the brave one," Rifkatu sighed, her tears starting up again. "You are so bold to tell the people about God. I still can't believe how you responded to the terrorist leader yesterday when he questioned us if we were Christians."

"We have to be prepared, Rifkatu," Margaret whispered. "There are two things we are going to face. They will ask us to renounce Christ, and they will ask us if we are willing to marry a Boko Haram soldier. We cannot do either!"

Rifkatu nodded in the darkness, and Margaret felt her approval. "Let's pray," Margaret suggested. Sure enough, after praying for a while, both girls dozed off into a fitful sleep. They were totally exhausted from the day's terror. The morrow came quicker than they wanted.

The next morning Margaret had an idea. "Rifkatu, we are like Jonathan and David in the Bible. We have always been close. I want to give you something, just like Jonathan did to David, in case we get separated. Here, take my headpiece. It is my favorite. I have an extra one along. Every time you wear it, think of me and pray for me."

Rifkatu didn't know what to give her bosom friend in return. Then she remembered that she was wearing a double skirt. Unwrapping the first layer, she tearfully handed it to Margaret. "You take this, my sister, and remember me. Whatever happens to us, Margaret, we will be friends forever."

The plaza was swarming with girls wearing colorful dresses and wraparound headpieces. Though dirty and tired, the girls were still girls—and a handsome sight for a motley crew of love-starved warriors.

Surrounding the more than two hundred captive girls, dozens of Boko Haram soldiers meandered about nonchalantly, as if enjoying a morning stroll. Margaret trembled when she realized the men were examining them as if they were merchandise.

Beyond the people who milled in the plaza, gnarled trees circled them, and beyond that was the dreadful bush. *This is the awful Sambisa Forest,* Margaret sighed. *And what will happen with us poor girls now? We have to be bold . . .*

"Let's try to look ugly," Margaret hissed to her friend, trying to shield her face with her hands.

"I wish we could," Rifkatu answered, fear etched all over her attractive features. "Even if we could, I am sure it wouldn't help."

All the soldiers seemed to be looking down to the end of the plaza where a huddle was taking place. Surrounded by bodyguards, two tall, dark-skinned men dressed in impeccable camouflaged fatigues were discussing the future of the Chibok girls. *It's as if they don't know what to do with us now that they have us securely in their grasp,* Margaret mused.

"Those two leaders look identical, like twins," Margaret whispered. "I am sure they are the two main Boko Haram leaders that everybody is afraid of."

Rifkatu nodded.

At that moment the two Boko Haram leaders joined the circle around the girls, sometimes stepping into the group to inspect some girl more closely. Just as Margaret feared, tall Rifkatu caught their attention immediately. The two men pushed their way through the cluster of girls till they stood in front of her. Rifkatu stood as still as a statue. Though well covered with her wraparound dress, her beautiful facial features and her sculptured figure had caught the men's attention. Her large, dark eyes were full of terror.

They don't even look at me! Margaret realized. *I feel so sorry for Rifkatu.*

As they led Rifkatu away, Margaret's heart felt like breaking. Rifkatu's eyes caught Margaret's, and they locked harder and longer than ever before. Margaret cried again. *I will never forget those eyes,* she vowed. *They will haunt me forever!*

Just before the two leaders were out of hearing distance, Margaret distinctly heard one say to the other, "This will be a good one for the commander stationed in Gwoza. He told me he needs a younger wife since his other two are getting old."

Several other girls were carefully selected from among the group, and Margaret soon saw that only the bigshots were getting their pick that day.

Suddenly the soldiers divided the swarm of girls down the middle, and half of them were led away. Approximately one hundred girls were loaded back onto the trucks and taken away. The remaining girls later discovered that their classmates had been taken to another Boko Haram camp that lay closer to Chad.

After the other girls had been taken away, Margaret's group was led into the village to an open plaza where other Boko Haram slaves had huge pots of porridge ready for them. The porridge consisted of corn flour cooked with water and flavored with tamarind juice and sugar. The girls were starving and the porridge went down well.

Kind ladies from among the captives also showed the girls two large adobe houses next to the plaza that would be their homes. They also offered the girls water for bathing. Though the girls were still in shock, they went through the motions of taking care of their basic physical needs, and the caring captives were there to do what they could to help. Next the girls were divided into two groups, one for each house. At dusk they were locked in. They found stacks of Muslim prayer rugs, apparently for them to sleep on. After finding places for their mats, the girls cried themselves to sleep, their emotional needs raw and unattended.

The next day the hundred girls in Margaret's group were taken to the plaza again. Filled with terror, they were almost certain what was about to take place. But to their surprise, only the emir showed up with a few bodyguards who always followed the leaders wherever they went. Instead of picking out more girls, the leader started preaching Islam. "My name is Abubakar Shekau, and that's why this village is called the Shekau Camp," the gun-toting terrorist announced, smiling his malicious smile through his thick black beard. "And now that you are here, you might as well accept that I am one hundred percent Muslim and that I am the boss."

The girls were quiet.

"You Christians have lived in ignorance way too long," Abubakar shouted, pacing back and forth in front of the mass of girls. "Now that you are here in the Sambisa Forest, you will be enlightened. You will discover that Allah is the only true God and that Sharia law is what we have to live by. This is a Muslim camp, and that's why we are asking you to convert to Islam today."

The girls who stood in the plaza, full of dread and with their heads bowed, were all from Christian families. Since they had attended an EYN high school, most of them belonged to the EYN church. Though not all of them were dedicated Christians, all the girls were fiercely opposed to the idea of converting to Islam. What the leader knew, and decided to capitalize on, was the girls' fear and vulnerability.

"How many of you are willing to convert to Islam?" Abubakar bellowed, stopping right in the front of the group.

The silence that followed was startling. Not even the forest birds sang. It was as though all of Borno State was quiet, waiting to see how this drama would unfold.

"How many of you are willing to renounce Christ?" Abubakar cried again, glowering at the girls.

Silence.

"Why don't you talk?" he snarled. "If you know what's good for you, answer!"

Margaret's heart was burning. *But what is there to say? If he forces us and we refuse, things will be bad. He might even kill us!*

"All right, here's another question," Abubakar yelled. "How many of you refuse to renounce Christ?"

Margaret knew what she had to do. Hoping against hope that the rest would do the same, she lifted her hand high.

After Margaret raised her hand, she lifted her face to peep at the other girls. Her heart warmed when she saw several other girls raising their hands as well.

"All of you that raised your hands, step over here," Abubakar commanded, pointing to one side of the plaza.

Margaret obeyed, and seventeen others followed. Standing bravely with her head held high and with tears in her eyes, Margaret wondered at how few girls were prepared to die for Christ.

To everyone's surprise, Abubakar seemed to ignore the eighteen girls—at least at first. He barked some orders to some of the soldiers who took the rest of the girls back to the houses where they would be held as captives. Among the things he commanded was an order that made Margaret's heart shudder. "Tell Madame Hannatu to give them each a hijab right away. Tomorrow we will start teaching them the prayers!"

As the girls filed away toward the camp's makeshift living quarters, Abubakar yelled after them. "And remember to wear your hijabs at all times. It's for modesty. If you wear your hijabs and cover your bodies properly, the soldiers won't be tempted to molest you."

The girls understood the message, though a strange feeling came over them. What they didn't understand was why Abubakar was laughing so maliciously as he gave them the seemingly solemn warning.

After the eighteen girls were alone with Abubakar, Margaret expected a showdown, and maybe even death. She had heard many stories of what Boko Haram did when Christians wouldn't renounce Christ. Although she was ready, she found herself trembling like a leaf in the wind.

However, to the girls' surprise, he seemed civil, almost kind. "Why won't you renounce Christ?" he asked.

Margaret answered for the eighteen. "Because He is our Lord and Savior. He died on the cross for our sins. Why would we want to renounce such a Friend? We love Him!"

Margaret could see that Abubakar wasn't impressed with her little sermon, but she didn't care. She just knew what she had to say, and then chose to remain silent.

Abubakar explained how converting to Islam was not easy and that it would take time. Even as he talked, the girls knew the ordeal was far from over and that he would not be satisfied until they were all wearing a hijab and praying to Allah. *At least he is not going to kill us today,*

Margaret sighed, relieved.

After the session was over, Abubakar ushered the girls back to camp and they faced their third day in the Sambisa Forest. They already missed their families fiercely, especially since they didn't know if they would ever see them again. But Margaret led the group in accepting their fate and making the best of their situation.

The fourth day in the Sambisa Forest was by far the worst so far. What happened was something the girls had feared from the beginning but only now took place. Dozens of soldiers showed up at the plaza, looking at the girls, deciding which one they wanted. Abubakar kept the eighteen beside him at the head of the plaza protectively, for reasons Margaret couldn't understand, but she was relieved nonetheless.

The rest of the Chibok girls who now stood on display in the plaza were transformed. They all wore brown, gray, or black hijabs that hung all the way down to their ankles.

All the soldiers could see to make their choice of a wife was the face that peered out of the hijab's window. Abubakar was overseeing the selecting. Every time a soldier finally decided which girl he wanted, there was a showdown.

"What is your name?" a skinny Boko Haram soldier asked the girl of his choice.

"Hawwa," the girl answered hesitantly, her eyes on the ground.

The soldier placed his finger under Hawwa's chin and brought her face up so she would look at him. "My name is Ibrahim. Will you marry me?" he asked, grinning maliciously.

"No!" Hawwa snapped, blushing through the window of her hijab and jerking her face away.

Hawwa knew that Abubakar was watching.

"If you don't marry me, Hawwa, you will become my slave. If you marry me, I will be kind to you and you will have the privileges of a wife. If you are my slave, I will beat you."

What can Hawwa do? Margaret moaned to herself, shaking her head. *The choices are so slim, and none of them are good.*

Margaret felt like running over to the poor girl to throw her arms around her, but Abubakar would tear her away and probably even beat her. All she could do was pray, so pray she did. Silently. In her heart she screamed out her agony as she watched Hawwa's drama.

"If you marry me, it won't be sin," Ibrahim explained. "But if you don't, you will still be my concubine, and that would be sin for you." At this, Hawwa—and later many of the other Chibok girls—felt her resolve crumbling.

Fighting back a flood of tears, she nodded.

Ibrahim immediately called Abubakar over, who then asked Hawwa, "Will you marry Ibrahim?"

Slowly she nodded.

"No," Abubakar barked. "Say it out loud."

"Yes," Hawwa choked.

Abubakar, who had been carrying a prayer rug, threw it onto the ground and commanded, "Kneel here."

Hawwa knelt down beside a man she didn't even know, let alone love. Though she didn't want to, she knew she would have to marry him.

The prayer Abubakar intoned was in Arabic, and Hawwa didn't understand a word. It sounded hollow, and it was soon over. But in the eyes of Boko Haram, she was now a married woman. She followed her husband back into the village.

Margaret, who had watched it all, knew that Hawwa's heart was breaking. *And so is mine,* she sobbed. *How can this be happening to us?*

Another Boko Haram soldier approached the girl of his choice. "Will you marry me?" he asked briskly.

"No, I am married," Deborah answered.

"Don't lie to me," snapped her would-be suitor. "If you were in high school you are not married."

"Yes, she is married," Margaret announced boldly, stepping up closer. "And not only is she married, but she is with child."

"I was recently married," Deborah explained, blushing deeply, her head hanging. "My husband agreed that I finish my schooling. And yes, I am expecting a child . . ."

The soldier was bewildered, looking from Deborah to Margaret, not sure what to believe. Suddenly he turned on his heel, and spat, "I don't want anything to do with you!"

Soon he found another girl who struck his fancy, taking her as his slave as she refused to marry him.

One girl got angry and slapped her suitor in the face. Immediately Abubakar motioned to his bodyguards. They grabbed the poor girl by her arms, hauled her off into the forest, and beat her. When they were done, she was more than ready to be a wife, or a slave. *There really isn't that much difference!* Margaret concluded. *And what will I do when my turn comes?*

Naomi was a short, feisty girl from Chibok whom Boko Haram was not able to crush. She was picked from among the group of eighteen despite the fact that they were held separately and were not wearing hijabs. The Boko Haram soldier who chose her was shocked when Naomi resisted like a wildcat. She had not only refused to renounce Christ the day before, but now, standing with the eighteen, she also flatly refused when the suitor asked to marry her.

Leaving Naomi alone to think about the proposal, the jilted soldier wandered around among the other girls as if trying to find a better option. Eventually he came back and asked Naomi again, "So what is your decision about this marriage?"

Naomi answered boldly, "No, I do not want to get married. You kidnapped me and brought me here to Sambisa, and now you are talking to me about marriage. How can I get married here? It would be impossible. My mother and my father, my brothers and my sisters, and even my aunts and uncles aren't here. They don't even know what's going on."

Naomi's suitor stood in front of the girl, not knowing what to do to break her will. Naomi took advantage of the pause and continued, "If I say no, what will you do? If I say I do not want to get married, but want to serve God, will you let me go? Isn't that a good thing?"

"No," the Boko Haram soldier responded stubbornly. "It is a bad thing. Marrying me is a good thing!"

The suitor must have really liked the outgoing young girl. He called Abubakar onto the scene. Pointing his finger into Naomi's face, Abubakar warned her, "If you don't marry this man, or renounce Christ, I will have you killed!"

"That's fine," Naomi retorted. "If I renounce Christ I am as good as dead anyway. So kill me now!"

Abubakar had Naomi beaten, but she still refused to say yes or to kneel on the mat for the awful prayer that would seal her fate. Her suitor finally gave up and chose another girl. A whimpering Naomi edged up to Margaret, and Margaret put her arm around her and comforted her till the horrible ordeal was over.

Two dozen other girls were either married or led away as slaves that awful day.

That night, once they were locked into their prison house and on their mats ready to sleep, Margaret asked Naomi, "I wonder why the rest of us eighteen were not for sale today?"

"Because we are Christians!" Naomi snapped. "And we don't wear hijabs."

"Today I am glad that we Christians are an undesirable lot," Margaret replied. "I guess the reason they wanted you even if you are still an infidel is because you are just too cute."

Naomi shrugged. "I don't know why they chose me, but I'll tell you one thing—my back sure hurts tonight."

"Let's remember," Margaret added, "Boko Haram will still try to break us so we renounce Christ. We have to be on guard."

All the girls agreed.

A girl named Lylian sat up on her mat and said, "Margaret, you know that even if we didn't stand with you eighteen that first day, we did not renounce Christ in our hearts. I am just as much a Christian now as I was before. But yes, seeing how you were protected today, I wish I would have joined your group."

"God has forgiven you, Lylian," Margaret answered quickly. "Besides, our turn might still come. We will see. Let's just all be faithful, and we will see what the Lord will do to deliver us." One by one the girls fell into a troubled sleep.

Life became routine for the Chibok girls. After their morning porridge, it was time to pray. All of the girls, except the eighteen, were forced to kneel and learn the Islamic prayers. They were always asked to kneel on mats that Boko Haram provided, facing toward the east in neat rows of ten girls abreast.

The eighteen girls were always asked to stand by to watch the prayer sessions. It was an impressive scene to see row after row of almost a hundred girls, dressed in their flowing hijabs, bowing with their heads to the ground, then rearing back up repeatedly to lift their hands in prayer. A man who stood in front of them hollered out the words and showed the motions, and the girls were supposed to repeat them in low tones.

At first the Chibok girls tried not to repeat the Islamic prayer, but to pray to God in their hearts. It didn't work. The man leading the prayer would shout, *"Inna lillahi wa inna illeirajima la illa ha illallahu, Allahu Akbar!"* [1]

The girls repeated the prayer with their foreheads pressed to the ground. While they were going through the whole set of prayers, a man slipped between the rows of bowing girls. If he caught any of them not praying

---

[1] "From Allah we came and to Allah we will return. Allah is the greatest!"

to Allah, or silently praying to God, they would get hauled out into the woods and flogged. Although it took several days, the girls caught on, and the daily floggings stopped.

After prayer time, their main preacher tried to teach the Koran to the girls. He tried to explain why the Koran was so important. "The Koran is our sacred book!" he exclaimed earnestly. "It is the word of God as dictated to Muhammad by the archangel Gabriel and written down in Arabic. It speaks to us about all aspects of human existence, including matters of doctrine, social organization, and legislation. That's why you not only need to learn what the Koran has to say, but you must memorize it and obey it . . ."

The next hour was frustrating for both the preacher and the girls. The eighteen suffered as well, watching the impossible situation. How can an angry man teach something that is dead and cold to a group of uninterested girls? This session became one of the worst times of the day for all involved.

One morning the preacher opened the Koran and read a passage that said anybody kidnapped in jihad immediately became the property of their captors. At that moment the realization came over the girls. The Boko Haram terrorists had, in their view, the right to do whatever they wanted with the captive girls.

That night Naomi wrote in her diary, "Today the preacher again explained how we are Boko Haram's sole property and they can do with us what they want. He said they gave us hijabs so the soldiers couldn't see our bodies and have lustful thoughts. If we don't wear hijabs the soldiers might do bad things to us."

When not in religious training, the girls sewed clothes for themselves, cooked their own food, hauled in firewood from the forest, washed their clothes, and helped the other captives with the general work in the camp. They didn't have to cook for the soldiers, and for this Margaret was glad. Apparently their wives or slaves did their cooking. The soldiers only came around the girls' building when one of them needed a wife.

Despite the fact that the eighteen girls were not available for marriage, their lot was still difficult. They were constantly being ridiculed for their stupidity. The prayer leader, the preacher, and Abubakar were putting them under tremendous pressure to convert. "Look at your companions who converted. They are happy. They are learning about Allah. They are treated nicely. You are suffering only because you want to."

Then one day Abubakar drove up to the girls' quarters with several metal containers in the back that resembled gasoline cans. After calling the eighteen girls together and lining them up, he looked at them smugly. "Have you decided to renounce Christ by now?" he growled.

The girls shook their heads.

Motioning toward the gasoline cans, Abubakar made an announcement, a wicked grin on his face. "Then today I am going to burn you alive!"

Margaret was shocked. She didn't know what to believe because Abubakar's eyes were gleaming as if he were a child getting a birthday prize. *This is not for real*, Margaret thought desperately. *This is just another hoax, a scare tactic. I will not yield!*

The ordeal didn't last long. After fifteen minutes of taunting the girls and torturing them emotionally, Abubakar sneered, "Here, take these jugs of water for your baths." After the girls unloaded the cans, he jumped into the pickup and roared away.

In this way, the eighteen were slowly being worn to a frazzle.

One morning about three weeks after the girls had been taken captive, Abubakar showed up after prayers and the Koran reading had ended. For once he tried to behave courteously as he presented himself to the group of girls. "I have a surprise for you this morning," he beamed, stroking his bushy beard and pacing back and forth in front of them. "You have been doing well. You are learning to pray to Allah.

You are memorizing the Koran. You wear your hijabs faithfully. So I have decided to give you a gift. I am planning a special trip for you to see your parents next week."

At first the girls were stunned. Then they became very, very excited. Could this be true?

"I am thinking of having this grand meeting in Maiduguri," Abubakar continued. "I am still working out the details, but all your parents will come to meet you at the park we have chosen. After spending the day with you, they will be happy to see how well you are doing and will gladly let you return to this excellent place of spiritual education. Here you are not brainwashed by that horrid western education but are taught straight from Allah and the Koran."

The girls could hardly believe the good turn of events. Although Margaret constantly told the girls that she didn't believe Abubakar, she couldn't help but allow her hopes to build up with the rest. Almost every day Abubakar came and explained how the plans were coming along.

One morning Abubakar made a shocking announcement. "One thing I need to tell you though, girls, is that I can only take you to see your parents if you are wearing a hijab. Can you imagine how it would look if we would meet your parents in Maiduguri and eighteen were not cooperating with this Muslim requirement? It would not look right. But don't worry, as long as you wear a hijab and join in the prayers and the memorizing of the Koran, you can go."

Margaret's heart sank. *This is a trick,* she decided, anger churning in her heart. *But will the rest actually believe it?*

Then, turning to the eighteen who always stood out, Abubakar continued, "You still have several days to decide. The trip is planned for next Sunday. Your parents are aware of it and are as excited as you are. I sent them videos to show how happy you are here, and they really want to see you and give Boko Haram their support."

Most of the girls believed Abubakar. He had been taking videos of them lately during prayer time and the Koran reading. That's why most of the eighteen immediately wanted to wear a hijab. They were tired of constantly standing up to the Islamic pressures at camp. But Margaret and Naomi stood their ground—at first.

In the end, it was Lylian who presented the argument that finally convinced them to make the change.

"Look," Lylian explained, "the rest of us girls are not converted to Islam. We're only pretending to pray to Allah. You know that we are really praying to God. And, Margaret, what does it matter? You yourself said that God forgives us. If you would change, we would all be the same. Everything would be easier for all of us, and we could go see our parents."

The voice of the majority prevailed, though Margaret doubted the promise and was not happy. By Sunday all the girls, including Margaret and Naomi, were wearing a hijab.

Sunday morning dawned bright and clear. It had rained the night before and the trees sprinkled through the village glistened green in the sunlight. The blue skies and a fresh breeze foretold a beautiful day for the promised trip.

All the girls met out in the plaza, dressed in the best clothes they had. All were dreaming about meeting their parents. Excitement penetrated the plaza like the sunshine that warmed everything under its glare.

The prayer leader soon showed up for their morning prayers. *We will probably travel to Maiduguri after the prayers,* the girls assumed. For the first time, the eighteen joined the rest, kneeling in neat rows and saying the prayers that even they had memorized by now.

The girls expected Abubakar to show up after the Koran reading and memorization, ready to take them on the memorable trip to Maiduguri. When he didn't appear, Margaret approached the religious teacher as he left the plaza and asked, "What about the trip to Maiduguri to see our parents?"

The teacher grinned at them maliciously. "The trip did not work out after all, and Abubakar had to cancel it."

Every single girl's eyes watched the teacher closely. Not one of them said a word.

Then, allowing his eyes to show his glee, the teacher blurted out, "Furthermore, your parents decided they didn't want to see you after all."

Leaving the girls speechless, he turned on his heels and left.

The girls were devastated. They all stood in one huge huddle and wept. The girl who took it the hardest was Margaret. "I should have tried harder to convince you girls that this was a trick," she wailed. "I should have prepared you for this letdown. But even I wanted to believe that ridiculous story. All they wanted was to get the rest of us to wear a hijab and to start converting to Islam. And they got what they wanted because none of us will dare take off our hijab now. They would kill us for sure."

The girls stared at Margaret, knowing that every word she said was the truth.

"But look," Margaret continued, putting on a brave smile, "we can't let this get us down! What's done is done. Let's cheer up and make the best of our lives here in this horrible place! There are better days ahead . . ."

All of the girls looked at Margaret, seeking direction. Margaret looked around and saw the two guards Abubakar had assigned to watch them. They were sitting on a log, out of earshot from the girls. Margaret spoke again. "I have been thinking about an idea that we need to make happen right away."

"What is it?" Deborah asked expectantly.

"You know we don't have even one Bible here at this camp. And we need God's Word badly."

"That's true," Deborah acknowledged. The girls had dropped the few Bibles they had on the road so the people from Chibok could follow them after their kidnapping.

"We're going to reconstruct as much of the Bible as we can," Margaret explained in hushed tones. "Let's watch for any slip of paper we can find. Some of the food that Boko Haram brings us is packed in paper or cardboard. And the little Koran workbooks have blank pages. So let's gather all the paper we can. We also have a few pencils and pens. Let's write down what we can remember of Scripture."

"I know Psalm 91 by memory," Naomi said with sudden realization. "I can write that down."

"And I know Psalm 23," Deborah added.

"I memorized the book of Ephesians," Margaret informed the group. "Let's see how much of the Bible we can come up with. Then whenever we meet secretly to pray, we can read Scripture to each other for encouragement."

Several weeks after the girls' crushing disappointment, Abubakar changed their guard.

"It's because Abubakar finally sees that we are not planning to escape," Margaret explained to her friends one morning when they met in the clearing after their morning chores. "And Old Friday, our new guard, trusts us and lets us have some privacy."

Even as the girls talked, excitement running high among them, Old Friday sat on a log at the edge of the clearing, out of hearing distance. Apparently he wasn't paying any attention to the girls. He seemed to be napping, his head cradled against the immense tamarind tree that stood like a sentinel between the clearing and the camp.

The girls pulled out their papers and began to write. They reconstructed large portions of Scripture and read them in what was fast becoming their morning devotions. Besides this, they were also compiling a small songbook. Suddenly Naomi raised a Koran workbook and announced gleefully. "I am starting to keep a diary. I have written our whole story, starting from the day we were kidnapped. It is for remembrance. Someday someone will want to read our story."

"That's great!" Margaret agreed, nodding vigorously. "We will forget many details if we don't write them down. I will also start a diary immediately." Several others decided to do the same.

Suddenly life in the Sambisa had a purpose. It was a new challenge the girls relished, not only to sneak precious moments to write Scripture by memory and write in their diaries, but also to read to each other in secret moments of joy. Margaret sneaked in a few minutes for them to pray, even if it meant keeping their eyes open in case someone dropped by.

The girls also found moments to write, read, and pray in the privacy of their bedrooms. They had to stay alert in the bedrooms because if some Muslim child or slave popped in, they could be caught. But it was their times in the clearing, where they could easily see anybody approaching, that they especially relished.

"At least there's one good thing about these huge hijabs," Naomi giggled, clutching her diary to her breast. "We can hide our precious writings under our clothes, and no one will find them."

"It's time to prepare our noonday meal," Margaret announced, getting up from a stump she had been sitting on. "Let's go get that taken care of."

The other girls followed suit.

"Let's race!" Lylian shouted. She picked up her long skirt and took off for their house, her long, graceful legs eating up ground like a gazelle on a savanna.

Margaret, though she ran as fast as she could, could not catch up with Lylian. She gave up once she was abreast with the tamarind tree and their elderly guard.

"You girls are happy today," Old Friday told her with a toothless grin. His little straw hat was cocked just a little and his big brown eyes twinkled. The many wrinkles in his face fascinated Margaret.

"I guess we are," Margaret chuckled. "And just a little frisky this morning. But hey, why not? Things could be worse."

As Margaret continued toward the house, the old man shook his head. As he watched her, a deep frown etched across his forehead. *It is not right that they keep these virgins back here in this horrible place! These girls were made to be free and happy in their own homes. May God save them, because though I wish I could help them, I know I can't!*

One morning after having been in the camp for seven months, Margaret and several other girls approached Old Friday with a few questions that were burning in their hearts. "Friday, why is it that Abubakar is not placing us with marriage partners anymore?" Margaret inquired. "And why is it that you are taking care of us instead of the guards?"

Old Friday seemed as old and gnarled as some of the baobab trees standing nearby. As usual, he wore a little narrow-brimmed straw hat and a toothless grin. For some reason the kind little man didn't seem to fit in the camp, and the girls often wondered if he was a genuine disciple of Boko Haram, or a captive doing his job by force as they were.

Old Friday took his time, thinking, with a faraway look in his eyes. "I am not sure about everything, Margaret. I only hear whiffs here and there. One reason I know for sure is that Abubakar wants to make a deal with the government, and you girls are his collateral. He wants two things in exchange for you: a lot of money and the release of some of his cronies who are in prison."

"That makes sense," Margaret nodded. "He doesn't want us to marry because then we wouldn't be free once the deal is made. Also, he wants to have us in good shape."

"Is that why he is constantly taking videos of us lately?" Deborah blurted out, nodding knowingly.

"Absolutely!" Friday smiled. "You are good propaganda. You are his future gold mine. And once his money runs out, he will use you."

"His trump card," Lylian sneered. "That's all we are! At least we get better treatment this way, and we aren't forced to marry."

"There's another thing I suspect." Friday grinned pensively, wrinkling his forehead more than it already was. "I think he likes you girls . . .

Chibok Girls

He seems jealously protective of you. Did you ever think of it that that might be the reason he only lets me guard you?"

"I have noticed how he doesn't allow any soldiers get close to us anymore," Naomi agreed, a little grin playing on her puckered lips. "At least that's a blessing."

"Also, I heard say that one of you is related to him," Friday chuckled. "All I know is that he likes you and that makes you the luckiest girls who have ever been captive in the Sambisa Forest."

"I sure wonder which one of us is related to Abubakar," Naomi wondered, a frown chasing away any hint of a smile. "I hope it's not me . . ."

"Wow!" Margaret exclaimed. "I will tell you one thing. The fact that we are protected is not an accident. And it's not because Abubakar is a good man. It is a gift from God to His daughters. We are the daughters of the King!"

All the girls nodded in agreement.

Although they were still captives and their future was uncertain at best, things at the moment seemed to be going amazingly well for the girls. What Margaret had no way of knowing, however, was that far away two very sad things were happening—to her mother and to her best friend, Rifkatu.

Part three
Will it Ever End?

*S*oon after Margaret had been kidnapped, her mother became ill and battled with high blood pressure for a year. Eventually her kidneys failed, and on June 4, 2016, a little over a year after Margaret was abducted, she died. Though the doctors diagnosed her with various sicknesses, anyone close to her knew the real cause of her death—a broken heart.

After Rifkatu had been taken away to become the wife of the commander from Gwoza, Margaret thought of her best friend often and prayed for her every day. Little did she know that she would not see her friend for more than three years. Perhaps it was better that Margaret didn't know it, but when Rifkatu was taken to Gwoza, she was accompanied by four soldiers. And what happened on that trip was so horrible that we will gently pull the curtain over the brutal scenes.

Rifkatu refused to marry the commander, so her life became a horrible nightmare as a concubine of a Boko Haram commander who already had two wives. About nine months after that horrific trip from Sambisa Forest to Gwoza, she had a little baby boy.

One day not long after their discussion with Old Friday, the girls were ordered to all line up in the plaza. Numbly the girls looked at each other. They all knew what was happening—another Boko Haram big-shot needed a wife. Abubakar and the commander spent all the time they wanted looking at and talking to the girls. They didn't seem to mind that the girls were trembling from head to foot, and some were crying. *Who will it be this time?* was the scream in each one's heart. *Will it be me?*

The commander chose Lylian.

Deborah took this especially hard, as she loved Lylian. In addition, Deborah was preparing herself for the arrival of her baby, though no one seemed to notice because of her huge hijab. *Oh, I wish my husband were here to take care of me! Or better yet, that I could be back in my beloved village with my family and husband.*

Though Deborah knew several good midwives lived among the captives, she still dreaded to have her baby in the Sambisa Forest. *At least I don't have to take care of a Boko Haram husband like Lylian does,* she sighed thankfully.

That night Deborah gave birth to a healthy little boy. She named him Toma.

Slowly the afternoon sun dropped lazily toward the western horizon. As a group of long-tailed glossy starlings made a raucous din in the trees above, several ladies were tending two steaming iron pots, each set on three stones placed around an open fire.

In one pot, water was bubbling like the crater of some angry volcano. In the other, Margaret was making draw soup.[1] She crushed the dry baobab leaves in the wooden mortar, slamming the pestle up and down to the rhythm of the starlings' calls. "When I used to make draw soup at home, we had everything it took to make it delicious," she complained. "But here we can find only a few ingredients."

---

[1] A soup made of okra, spinach, and various edible leaves.

A girl named Damaris nodded as she tended the other pot and sprinkled handfuls of guinea corn flour into the boiling water. "That's right, Margaret," she agreed. "And the flour we have here to make the mush isn't nearly as good as the flour we could grind fresh every day at home."

Margaret sprinkled in a handful of *dauruwa*[2] seeds that she had smashed to powder in the mortar along with several dried hot peppers. "At least we have some of the basic flavorings that we can find in the wild," Margaret added cheerfully. "Imagine draw soup without dauruwa and hot pepper."

During the first year and a half of their captivity, the Chibok girls had enough food to eat. Every so often the Boko Haram soldiers came back from their raids with their pickups loaded down with all kinds of goodies. Sometimes they even had things like noodles, wheat flour, and Irish potatoes, luxuries even back in their hometowns. But if much time elapsed between raids, they were down to the basics, such as maize, guinea corn, and groundnuts.

After the guinea corn mush was thick, and the soup finger-licking good, Margaret called the girls together. Several were out in the bush collecting firewood, but most of them soon gathered, carrying little plastic bowls into which they ladled the soup.

After the mush was cool enough to handle, the girls crowded around and helped themselves to a handful. Using their fingers, they formed little globs of the thick mush and then made a hole in each one with their thumb. Each girl then plunged the little glob into her draw soup, filling the tiny crater to the brim before popping it into her mouth.

For a minute they ceased their chatter, busy filling their stomachs. The nourishing African favorite had a strong flavor of alfalfa. "Can there be anything better than draw soup?" Deborah purred. Then she teased her friend good-naturedly. "Not because you made it, Margaret, but in

---

[2] A flavorful small brown seed from the locust tree.

spite of it, right?"

The girls were eating quietly when Lylian walked up from the section of the village where the married soldiers lived. "I was wondering if you would have some extra red peppers?" she inquired, smiling at the girls.

"Sure," Margaret answered, happy to see their friend who seldom came around since she was married. "How has it been going for you?"

"Not too bad," Lylian sighed. She looked at the group of girls, fondly remembering how she used to be a part of them. She still loved them very much. "I must say my husband treats me better than I expected. He hardly lets me work at all since we have so many slaves to do the work. He spoils me with jewelry and goodies."

Seeing the girls' frowns, she added, "But of course, I would still prefer living here with you girls."

The girls nodded, happy that things weren't worse for her.

As Lylian was ready to leave, she announced, "Oh, and guess what—I'm expecting a baby!"

The girls' hearts were torn. In one way they were happy for Lylian, and their eyes told her as much. But they also couldn't bear the thought that their dear Lylian was living with one of their antagonizers.

Before the girls could congratulate their friend, a loud shriek rent the quiet of the evening. From the bush beyond the plaza, several girls came running, the one in the center clutching her hand and screaming as she ran.

"Oh, no!" Margaret exclaimed in alarm. "Not a snakebite!"

A girl named Vashti had gone to gather firewood for the morning's porridge. Reaching down to pick up a dry stick in the brush, she didn't see the awful carpet viper[3] that was coiled and ready to strike. It bit her right on her knuckle.

---

[3] *Echis ocellatus*, or West African carpet viper, is a thick, strong, aggressive viper. It is named after its distinct markings that resemble a carpet. It is highly venomous and is responsible for more snakebite deaths in Africa than all other snake species combined.

The draw soup forgotten, Margaret and several other girls rushed Vashti off to the camp's makeshift hospital. Just as Margaret feared, they had no antivenin for the poor girl. Several hours later, she died.[4]

Several Boko Haram soldiers buried Vashti on a plot of ground where they had buried many others. There were no gravestones or markings of any kind, only shallow graves and mounds of red dirt.

As they watched the burial, the girls longed to read the Scripture passages that were carefully concealed under their hijabs. Margaret thought of several songs about heaven that she would have loved to sing. But with some Boko Haram soldiers around the whole time, they didn't have a chance to even quote the verses. All they could do was watch the sad affair and stay quiet, tears streaming down their faces.

The next day they did what they were doing a lot lately. They asked Old Friday for permission to spend some time in the clearing. Though they were nervous about the possibility of snakes, they wanted to spend time reading Scripture. They pulled out their precious papers, memorizing as much as they could. They knew that at any time these precious papers could be taken from them.

The girls also sang several songs in low tones. Before they finished singing, several girls were weeping. They remembered Vashti and the wonderful times they used to have in church at home, singing joyfully on Sunday mornings.

Then the girls prayed. That day Deborah was chosen to keep her eyes open in case someone showed up. She held her little Toma to her breast and watched as she prayed.

The girls prayed earnestly, asking God for comfort because of the sadness they felt due to Vashti's death. As they prayed, they were comforted, remembering that Vashti was in heaven with Jesus instead of in the Sambisa with the Boko Haram.

---

[4] Two girls died of snakebites during the three years Margaret was in the Sambisa Forest. When Boko Haram reported instances of death to the public, they never reported snakebites.

Then Deborah hissed, "Someone is coming!"

Sure enough, a ten-year-old girl had wandered into the clearing. Deborah, who had gotten caught up in grieving for Vashti, had not noticed right away. After she left, Margaret explained, "That girl is a daughter of one of the soldiers! If she caught on that we were praying, we are in big trouble."

Sure enough, the next day after prayer and reading the Koran, two soldiers and Abubakar commanded Margaret to follow them out to the clearing. Then, after lecturing her about the foolishness of Christianity and blaming her for being the ringleader in keeping the girls from converting to Islam, Abubakar had a soldier beat her till her back was bleeding.

To her relief, however, they didn't find the precious Scriptures hidden under her clothes.

That was not the only time Margaret was beaten. The trouble usually popped up during prayer time and the reading of the Koran. The prayer leader and the Islamic teacher both knew that, in her heart, Margaret was loyal to Christ. They tried their best to catch her praying to God instead of to Allah, and when they saw that she didn't want to memorize the Koran, it made them furious. But Margaret pretended to be unable to memorize, and after three and a half years she had memorized only three chapters of the Koran. Meanwhile, however, she memorized every snitch of Scripture the girls could collect, including whole chapters.

Margaret paid a high price though. Again and again she was hauled into the clearing and beaten mercilessly. But every beating only made her more determined to stay loyal to Christ and not embrace radical Islam. *What religion forces people to pray by beating them when they don't want to?*[5]

---

[5] Today Margaret's back is still scarred from her many beatings.

NO TURNING BACK

Terror-stricken, the girls gazed toward the sky. A fighter jet screamed over the village where the girls were stationed, dropping bombs that were not only ripping up the village but also killing people. A cry was heard all through camp, "The army is bombing us! The army is bombing us!"

Not only the Chibok girls, but also the Boko Haram soldiers, started running frantically into the forest to seek shelter. After crashing through the bush for fifteen minutes, Margaret was tired and stopped under an immense tree, panting. Several whimpering friends joined her under the tree's canopy. "We might as well stop running," Margaret decided. "We are exhausted. If the bombs get us, we die and go to be with Jesus."

Just then another bomb ripped the brush about a hundred yards from where the girls stood. But instead of running, Margaret and the girls just cowered at the foot of the tree, praying. It was then that Margaret saw a sad sight. Abubakar came running past their tree, his legs pumping like the pistons of a revved-up motorcycle. His hair was disheveled, and his army cap was gone. His eyes were as big as saucers and full of terror as he rushed past. But what struck Margaret to the depths of her heart was that he was crying.

Watching him plow through the brush, Margaret suddenly discovered that she could no longer hate the man who had caused them so much grief and terror. Because of the love of Christ in her heart, she pitied him. To the shock of the girls around her, she cried out in anguish, "Lord, have mercy. Abubakar is going to die without you!"

Abubakar had been sure the innocent women and children would serve as a shield to keep the Nigerian army from attacking them. He felt certain the hundreds of captives and slaves would protect him from bombing raids. But it didn't work. The army dropped the bombs anyway.

Five of the Chibok girls went home to be with Jesus that day, and many captives and several dozen soldiers died as well. Because of this tremendous blow, conditions began to deteriorate for everyone in Camp Shekau.

The second year in the Sambisa Forest was a hard one for Margaret and her companions. The girls were greatly saddened when Lylian's baby, whom she called Amina, died before she was able to see the light of the sun. After Amina's death, the girls' loneliness and homesickness for their families grew by leaps and bounds. As they went through the routines of each day, things only got worse. *Will this hell on earth ever end?* Margaret wondered. Again and again she found herself crying out to God.

The only thing that kept Margaret and her friends going were those special hours in the clearing seeking God. Margaret also treasured the moments she spent alone with her Lord. Many a night she would weep into her pillow, "Lord, just help us to be faithful. And deliver us from evil, please. But not my will but yours be done."

It was an exceptionally beautiful morning. The first rains of the season had fallen and washed the hazy sky clean. The sun was shining brightly and the birds sang joyously. An Abdim's stork glided into a flaming mimosa tree on silent wing, landing on its big stick nest in the tree's crown. It dropped the stick it carried in its beak onto the already large pile and stepped on it. Soon the nest would be ready for eggs.

A low adobe wall enclosed not only the mimosa tree but also a sprawling adobe house and its bare courtyard. A young girl, wearing an enormous gray hijab, was dutifully sweeping the courtyard clean from the leaves that had fallen during the rain the evening before. As she swept, she sang softly, almost under her breath. It was not wise to sing Christian songs in the Sambisa Forest.

Margaret straightened her tired back and sighed. *This house was certainly a grand place in its day,* she mused. *Probably some well-to-do farmer lived here with his family. I wonder if they were happy. Since Boko Haram took over, no one can be happy anymore. Yet, because of Jesus, I can still sing.*

One morning everyone was startled to learn that three of the girls who had been forced to marry had escaped during the night. Abubakar was furious and questioned the single girls, threatening to lash them if they withheld any knowledge of their whereabouts. But the girls didn't know anything, so he finally gave up.

As Margaret swept and sang, her heart cheered for the three friends. *I am so glad Lylian managed to escape. And poor Rekiya who is heavy with child. How can she travel?* She thought of Miriam, whose darling six-month-old boy she held whenever she had a chance. *God bless them and protect them as they run. I wonder how they are managing. Maybe sometime soon I can escape as well.*

Two days later, however, the three girls were returned to the Sambisa Forest. They told the rest of the girls their story. On the morning after their escape, they had stumbled into one of the nearby villages. Hungry, they entered a store and asked for water and biscuits.

"Who are you and where do you come from?" the store owner asked, wary.

The girls answered, "We are of those girls that Boko Haram kidnapped in Chibok."

The store owner nodded, then blurted out, "Don't these girls belong to Abubakar Shekau? Aren't they his daughters?" He provided the girls and their babies with food and a place to sleep, but the next day he returned them to the Sambisa Forest.

That evening was a horrible one, not only for those who had escaped, but for all of the girls. The soldiers lashed the three young women mercilessly, insulting them and mocking them. The other girls were forced to hold Miriam's baby and watch. Pulling out their long machetes, the soldiers threatened to cut off the girls' heads. Though they didn't kill them, the barrage of emotional and physical damage the three girls received was almost more than a human being could bear.

After the attempted escape, the soldiers became much stricter, and the girls couldn't spend their precious time in the clearing in the forest anymore. Old Friday was joined now by two other soldiers who hung around the outskirts of their area in the camp—and inspired deathly fear in the girls.

As soon as dusk set in, the soldiers locked the girls into the two houses that had become their nightly prison. All this made life more difficult for the girls, but that was still not the worst.

Since the soldiers were too scared to make many raids, food was becoming increasingly scarce. The girls didn't know what all was happening behind the scenes, but the two Boko Haram leaders, Abubakar Shekau and Al-Barnawi, had had a fallout and worked separately now. The girls were constantly hearing rumors that things were not going well for Abubakar and his men.

Boko Haram had pillaged and partly destroyed a dozen villages toward the south and had held them under their control for some months, but now the tables had turned and they were being beaten on all sides. The Nigerian army was slowly chasing them back north where they had come from. For the Chibok girls, life became doubly hard as a result of this reverse for the terrorists.

Drops of sweat were sliding down Margaret's cheeks one morning as she dug for wild yams in an open area of the forest. The shovel was heavy and the sun was hot. "This is getting really bad," Naomi remarked with a sigh, picking up the yams that Margaret unearthed and putting them into an old sack. "Providing food for a hundred girls is not easy, is it?"

Margaret straightened and wiped the sweat from her face with her hijab that billowed down over her shoulders. "Yes, it is becoming harder and harder to find food. Nowadays most of our time is spent scrimmaging for food.

"And we are all getting skinny, aren't we? But one blessing we need to remember is that the soldiers never bother us," Margaret added, lowering her voice. "There are rumors of horrible things happening over in Al-Barnawi's camp. I often wonder why we are not molested."

Deborah, carrying her baby, had come along to watch. "Abubakar treats us like daughters," she said. "It's kind of a mystery, but he protects us jealously. I can sense that the soldiers do not dare touch us."

"All I can figure out," Margaret whispered, watching the distant guards out of the corner of her eye, "is that we are Abubakar's bargaining tool. Any way you look at it, it is a blessing from God for our protection."

"Exactly!" Naomi agreed, taking the shovel from Margaret for a turn at digging. "Let's just thank God, because I know it's a miracle straight from heaven. A direct answer to our prayers."

At noon another group of girls brought in leaves to make soup, but since there was no flour of any kind to make their needed mush, they ate a watery leaf soup and dipped in chunks of wild yam. This had to serve as their lunch.

That evening the girls were very discouraged and felt a strong need to pray. Though they were well aware of the risk, most of them assembled in the clearing. Margaret was tempted to take the chance of pulling out their little papers with scribbled Scripture, but then they saw the guards following them.

Some of the girls sat on logs. Some leaned against the trees. But many of them just sat on the ground. Even if they couldn't talk much, they were encouraged and comforted by each other's presence. "I guess we will go without supper again," Margaret smiled, trying to be brave. "I am not worried about myself, but I am worried about you, Deborah. You and your baby need nourishment."

"We are totally out of yams, or food of any kind," Naomi sighed, tears welling up in her eyes. "I don't know what to do for tomorrow. It is getting harder and harder to find yams. And I am tired of leaf soup!"

The girls were not afraid to talk about the food situation in the guards' presence, and they gave vent to their feelings. In a moment of desperation, one of the girls said, "I have a feeling we are going to starve!"

"What do you mean?" Naomi snapped. "We are already starving. We just haven't died yet!"

Then two things happened simultaneously: Some of the girls started to cry, and Abubakar walked onto the scene. The girls had been too engrossed in their discussion to see him approaching.

Some guard told him that we were congregated here again, Margaret realized. *Now we're in big trouble!*

Abubakar walked up close to the girls and looked from one to the next, as if wondering what to do. He had caught them crying and sensed their fear. He read discouragement all over their faces. Then, without saying a word, he turned on his heels and headed back to camp.

"What will happen now?" Margaret wondered aloud. "Will he have pity, or will he punish us? You can never know with that man. One day he treats us like *his girls,* as he calls us, and the next day he has us beaten till our backs bleed."

The next fifteen minutes were tense. Some of the girls wept. Others prayed. Then a soldier marched up and plopped a 25-pound bag of rice at Margaret's feet.

"Rice!" the girls cheered. "Rice for supper! Rice for a change!"

Deborah squeezed her little baby boy to her breast and wept. Miraculously, God had provided.

To this day, the Chibok girls don't know who tattled. Did Old Friday feel an obligation to honor his Muslim faith and tell Abubakar? The girls never knew for sure, but somehow the word got out that the girls' escapades to the clearing had to do with worshipping God. And someone told someone that they were hiding things written on paper under their clothes.

The raid came one morning just after the girls got up. First the soldiers burst into their houses, then they were followed by several women. The women went through all the girls' belongings as if with a fine-toothed comb while the soldiers watched. They found snippets of Scripture and diaries in many hideouts in the rooms.

But what was most embarrassing was when the women checked each girl's body. Fortunately the soldiers stepped outside for this. The women asked the girls to take off their clothes. They wanted to make sure they found every hidden paper.

There was one girl in the group who was rejoicing. She was the one who had come up with the idea of keeping diaries, and she had written much more than any of the others. Her whole story was hidden in her special hideout behind the house, tucked in a covered hole in the stone wall that surrounded the courtyard. That girl was Naomi.

Several girls who had papers on their bodies were beaten that day. Naomi felt sorry for the poor girls who were thrashed. She knew she was the one who should be beaten, since keeping a diary was her idea. But since the women didn't find anything on her, she got off scot-free. Later Naomi took it upon herself to comfort the girls, bathing their bruised backs with warm water.

After the raid, things were never the same. No one had Scriptures to read anymore except what was hidden in their memories. They couldn't meet in the clearing. And only during the night when everyone was asleep did Naomi get out her diary and write. And because finding a light source was a problem, it did not happen often. When Naomi could find a piece of a candle, or when the moon shone through the window, she wrote those things that were close to her heart.

Margaret and a few other girls also wrote in Naomi's diary occasionally. But Naomi was the one who watched over the little booklet closely as if her life depended on it. *This is for remembrance,* Naomi would say to herself again and again. *If we ever get back to civilization, this will help us remember so many things we would otherwise forget.*

Yelling and shouting from the plaza in the center of the village was a regular occurrence. Though the plaza was used for many different activities, it was often used by the soldiers for their exercising, drilling, and training. The girls avoided the plaza during these times, staying in their prison houses or going into the forest to forage for firewood or food.

It became a daily occurrence for the girls to hear the ruckus of the soldiers as they performed the antics of their crazy war cries and religious jargon. Many times, Abubakar himself filmed the activities or had others film him as he screamed the gospel of radical Islam into the camera's lens. Whenever he made the videos, he carried his guns and made threats. The girls heard rumors that some of these videos were sent to the government or posted online for all to see. The soldiers, many of whom were mere boys, got into a lot of horseplay and roughhousing as youngsters do.

Abubakar often made videos of the girls. One morning, as the soldiers looked on, Abubakar again got the girls together and lined up some of them for filming. This time he was livid.

"Look," he barked, his eyes crazed in anger. "The news is saying that we are molesting you girls and giving you a terrible rough life. As you well know, that is not true!"

Abubakar looked a fright. His eyes were like flames of fire. Spittle clung to his beard around his mouth as he continued his tirade. "Everyone is believing that big fat lie! All the infidels are making up stories about us. Even the president, and especially your parents, are hearing this false news. The army is fighting harder against us than ever before. May Allah curse them and punish them all!"

Calming down a little, he continued, "We have you here so we can teach you the ways of Allah. We are not mistreating you at all. I am going to take a video for the government that even your parents will see. I am going to prove that it is all a lie. That's why I want you to be happy and answer the questions I ask you. Then I want one of you to put in a plea to the government that they negotiate with us, to exchange you for our prisoners."

The girls didn't know what to do, so they obeyed. One by one Abubakar asked their names as they tried to smile. He also asked other questions about life at the camp. They were asked if they had been molested or mistreated.

The girls declared that they were being treated well. Then, at the end, each girl put in a plea for negotiations. "We miss our families and want to come home. Please negotiate so we can come home soon!"

After the video was taken, Abubakar was transformed. He practically danced around, bragging that the video would get the Nigerian government to the negotiating table, and that the deal was practically made.

Sure enough, in October of 2016, twenty-one girls were whisked away. Among them was Margaret's best friend, Naomi. Tucked under her clothes, she carried her precious diary.

With great difficulty, Margaret said goodbye to her friend. It was a blow for all the girls who had to stay. But among the eighty-two girls left in the special group that Abubakar treasured, there was new hope. Surely if God delivered the twenty-one, their turn would also come.

The early morning quiet of Shekau Camp was interrupted by the grating voice of a man on a loudspeaker: *"Allahu Akbar! Allahu Akbar! Allahu Akbar!"*

Margaret knew it was the Muslim prayer call. Though it was still dark and her watch read 4:30, she needed to get up soon to find her little pitcher of water and her mat for the first prayer session of the day.

She lay on her mat a little longer, shivering. And it wasn't from the cold, as it never gets cold in northeast Nigeria. She shivered because of the many questions racing through her mind as she lay there longing for a little more sleep. *What will happen to us?* she wondered. Things were not going well for Boko Haram. Yes, after the twenty-one girls left, there was food again for a while because Boko Haram had money again. But the money didn't last, and now the girls were constantly hungry again and were back to foraging for food in the forest like wild animals.

Deborah's little boy is healthy, but Deborah is thin, Margaret noted with worry. *Soon she won't have milk for her baby. And we don't hear anything about negotiations anymore.*

"Lord, our lives are in your hands. If we ever needed you before, we sure need you now!" she prayed, remembering a song she had learned in church. "And Lord, please take care of Naomi and her friends. I wonder if the girls are safe with their families, or was it some trick that Boko Haram pulled on us again?"

Seven months trekked by slowly after Naomi and her twenty friends were released. Every day became a major hurdle just to find enough food to stay alive. But the girls looked out for each other, and everyone especially took care of Deborah, whose little boy was growing fast.

Though the days were long, Deborah's daily dream seemed to sustain her. Many times a day she pictured herself arriving back in her hometown where she could find her husband and show him little Toma, who had been born in the Sambisa Forest.

Every day the Chibok girls waited, suffered, prayed, and dreamed on.

————————

Margaret's whole frame racked with sobs as she drank in the scene. In front of her were hundreds of beautiful Nigerian people—*normal* Nigerian people, dressed in bright colors and swarming toward her like a kaleidoscope of monarch butterflies. Margaret quickly crawled out of the vehicle that had brought the eighty-two Chibok girls to the rendezvous. Men and women came running, desperately hoping to meet their missing loved ones. Most of them were crying. Some were shouting with joy. Some were dancing. The eighty-two Chibok girls were meeting their parents and relatives for the first time in over three years.

Margaret herself was dressed like a normal African lady again. No drab hijab was draped over her to steal her identity. Instead, she was wearing a dress in bright orange and brown colors with a headpiece wrapped around her hair as before. It all made her feel so wonderfully Nigerian again.

Three days before, on May 6, 2017, the Chibok girls had been released, with an arrangement for them to come to the capital city of Abuja. There the president himself received them and gave them a warm welcome. The lead minister of the EYN Church in Abuja was also there to welcome them home. But most important, there was a commission of women there for a three-day session to prepare them for the homecoming.

To Margaret's joy, her friend Rifkatu's mother, Yanaf, was there to be her counselor. After hugging her and allowing her to cry on her shoulder, Yanaf gently told Margaret about her mother's recent death and prepared her for what she could expect once she got back home. Of course, Margaret was devastated at the news.

Then Yanaf asked the question Margaret was afraid she would ask. Straying from the counseling script, she quietly asked, "What do you know about Rifkatu? I was expecting her to be in the group with you."

Margaret couldn't answer. She just hid her face in her hands and cried.

"Please, Margaret, don't hide anything from me," Yanaf sobbed. "I want to know it all, even if it is horrible. Even if she is dead."

"Your daughter is alive," Margaret announced. "It's just so sad . . ."

Haltingly, Margaret told the brokenhearted mother what she knew.

Now the three-day counseling session was over and the girls were finally about to meet their families. Margaret jumped out of the vehicle to meet the multitudes, feeling glad and sad at the same time.

Margaret saw Deborah embracing her husband. She watched as the young mother proudly showed him his little son, Toma.

After embracing Lylian's mother, Margaret said, "Your daughter sent her greetings and wept because she could not come back with us. She told me to tell you that she is fine but misses you a lot."

Margaret saw most of her friends go to their mothers first, and suddenly the realization spread over her that she didn't have a mother to find. But she quickly found her brother Philip and ran to him. In his arms, she gave vent to more of her pent-up feelings. Slowly it was all coming out. All the terror and torture of those three long years was finally finding a release.

As Margaret slowly calmed down, her heart filled with appreciation and rejoicing. "O God, thank you, thank you!" she cried, almost beside herself with joy and relief for herself and her eighty-one sisters in Christ who were now free. "And because you kept us safe and brought us home safely, I have a debt I want to pay the rest of my life. It's a debt of love. I will love and serve you till the end of my days.

"And Lord," she sobbed, "don't let me ever forget the captives and slaves who are still back in the Sambisa Forest. Help me remember to pray for them daily. And if there is anything I can do for them, I am more than willing. Amen!"

Chapter 5

Already Dead

The small Nigerian village of Chikide cuddles up to the Mandara Mountain range where the highest mountain rears its peak 4,900 feet into the blue sky above the town. From Chikide, the Mandara's rocky peaks provide a fantastic picture for any viewer.

The Master Designer laid out this special mountain in three layers. Up till the year 2013, each layer was extremely important for the Gwoza farmers. One third of the way up the mountain, a large slash into its flank runs all along the mountain's side, creating a plateau perfect for planting crops. Two thirds of the way up the mountain there is a repeat, giving the mountain the look of a terraced garden designed for some giant agriculturalist.

But by far the most outstanding and life-giving part of the mountain is its flat top. This immense acreage is known among the locals for its fertile soil, opulent springs, and stunning views. Many years before, most of the villagers actually lived up on the mountaintop.

Yakubu Varda was a well-known farmer from Chikide. Though most of his memories were from the village, as a child he had lived up on the mountaintop. When he was nine years old, his family had followed the general populace as they moved down into the villages in the foothills. Here they would have easier access to bigger cities and modern conveniences.

"I was born up there on that mountain," Yakubu often told his six children when they sat out in the courtyard staring at the giant that was always there for them. "I used to play among those rocks strewn all over the mountain's contours. And, oh, the caves! There are hundreds of caves up there. We were scared to go inside, but we would often stand in the openings and hear the bats squeak."

Banner, Yakubu's fifteen-year-old son, took a special interest in his father's stories. He often imagined what life would have been like living up so high in the sky, and he shivered as he heard about the caves. Even in the foothills, the Mandara Mountains were dressed in a robe of millions of rocks, and caves popped up all over. Like his father, Banner had often stood uneasily at a cave's opening, listening to the bats' refrain.

"You should hear the story about the Old Man of the Mountain," Yakubu told his children one evening. "He died when he was almost a hundred years old, and they claim he never once came down off the mountain."

"Dad, that can't be!" Banner exclaimed. "Surely he would have come down sometime."

"He was kind of a hermit," Yakubu explained. "And according to the stories, he never touched foot in the valley. They even buried him up there, so he really was a mountain man."

Chikide was a quiet little village, and Yakubu was happy to raise his family there. But times were changing, and those peaceful moments spent out in the courtyard talking about the Mandara Mountains were not so common anymore. "I am really concerned about the new group called Boko Haram," Yakubu told his family one evening out in the courtyard. He had been talking to his sons, but now his wife Naomi had joined them, sitting on a mat like the others. Fourteen-year-old Suzanna was there as well, waiting uneasily to hear what her father had to say about the perilous times in which they were living.

"It all started so innocently," Yakubu remembered. "A Muslim revival they called it. Islamic teachers came into the villages, inviting the Muslim youth to their classes. They claimed they were only preaching Sharia law and the Islamic faith. But it is no secret that they were talking more and more about killing the infidels. I knew from the start that it was from the devil!"

"Yes," Banner agreed heartily. "I'd see them around all the time. They'd meet in the Muslim mosques and drink black coffee and eat dates."

"That's probably all they could afford," Yakubu grunted bitterly. "It seems they were mostly from the poorer class and often dressed in tatters. Dates are cheap and coffee is easy to come by. I think that's why they were often so skinny."

"They never invited us to their meetings because they knew we were Christians," added Tizhe, Yakubu's firstborn son. "Now these same youth are out killing left and right. Even some of our friends are into it. I can hardly believe it!"

"You have to understand, sons, that the Islamic law states that anybody who doesn't embrace Islam is an infidel and deserves to die," Yakubu explained. "And we as Christians are targets because we believe in Christ. They hate Christ."

"They also teach that if you die in jihad you go straight to heaven," Naomi added.

"What's jihad?" Suzanna asked, wide-eyed.

"That is what they call their holy war," Naomi explained. "It's when they fight for Allah's sake. For them, killing Christians is good because it is fighting for the truth. So if they get killed in jihad, they think they get rewarded greatly."

"Yes," Yakubu agreed. "Then the insurrection exploded several years ago in Maiduguri when Boko Haram and the army clashed. Then Boko Haram really showed their colors. But not until 2009, when almost a thousand people were killed, did northeast Nigeria really see what was brewing right under our noses—terrorism in the raw!"

"I am so glad Boko Haram has retreated into the Sambisa Forest," said Bulus, who was just older than Banner, a frown etched on his face. "At least now we don't have them under our noses like we did then."

"That's what you think," said Banner. "They say every village has people who support Boko Haram secretly."

"That's still not the worst," Yakubu explained earnestly. "The worst is that since they couldn't capture Maiduguri, they are coming south. In every town they enter they are pillaging, killing, and burning houses, businesses, and church houses. They are destroying village after village. The question that haunts me these days is, when will they hit Chikide?"

The courtyard was silent as everyone thought his own troubled thoughts. Yakubu surprised the boys when he announced, "Boys, I am seriously thinking of sending you five oldest to your uncle's place in Maiduguri soon. If Boko Haram hits Chikide, they will kidnap you and try their best to turn you into Boko Haram soldiers."

"But what will they do with the rest of you if you are captured?" Banner wailed. "I would be worried for Suzanna and especially for you, Dad. They would kill you!"

"They would if I wouldn't renounce my faith," Yakubu acknowledged seriously. "And you all know that I wouldn't do that. But I am an old man now, and you boys are young and full of life."

"I agree," Naomi whispered, tears welling up in her eyes. "They say Boko Haram is already approaching the outskirts of Gwoza, and that is way too close for comfort."

"I don't want to leave home," Banner stated, shaking his head. Then after pondering the situation, he added, "But if it's important that we go, I am willing."

That's how Yakubu's five oldest children, all of them boys, traveled to Maiduguri where they continued their studies. Yakubu and Naomi stayed behind to face the tense situation in Chikide with the three youngest, Suzanna, Habila, and Markus, who was only ten years old.

The three young men slipped into the cave's low entrance, bending over so as not to hit their heads on the header. Godwin, their guide, was practically running ahead, leading the way into complete darkness with only a dim flashlight.

It was terribly dark inside the cave. As that darkness embraced the group of young men, Banner felt afraid. But in spite of his fear, he plunged on, following Bulus, who in turn followed Godwin.

Suddenly the dark passageway stopped, and Godwin started climbing an almost perpendicular wall. Little rock ledges and pockets in the stone served as handholds and footholds. As they watched, Godwin soon reached the top and shone down so the two boys could follow.

Bulus climbed up first, slowly and carefully. Banner was surprised at how easy it was to climb the ten-foot rampart. Then they scuttled along another passageway of the cave that seemed even darker. Finally, after climbing up yet another steep section, the boys entered a large room of the cave that for once was illuminated.

Several lamps burned on niches in the cave walls. In the dim light Banner could see his family jumping up to receive them. His heart was overjoyed to see them again. He ran and embraced his mother first. Then he found his father and each one of his three younger siblings. It was a grand reunion.

As the family had suspected, Boko Haram had soon come to harass the village of Chikide, which had then become a ghost town. But now that Boko Haram was no longer controlling it as tightly as before, the villagers were sneaking back to their homes to replenish their supplies. Since Yakubu had contact with his sons by cell phone, he had suggested this visit. He enlisted Godwin, who lived in a cave close by, to go to Chikide to meet the boys and guide them to their hideout.

Banner was fascinated at how his parents had set things up in the cave to survive the crisis. Naomi did her cooking close to the cave's entrance because of the smoke, but inside the cave she had arranged things in a way that made everybody feel at home. She had placed rugs and mats to sit and sleep on, and she kept the smooth floor swept and clean. She had even brought several mottos from their home, and now they hung from the cave's rocky wall, reminding Banner of home. In the center of the room she had laid out the same big rug on which they had gathered to share meals before the crisis.

In preparation for the boys' visit, Naomi had made the best guinea corn mush and a delicious draw soup made from some spinach she had managed to gather from her garden at home. As they ate the simple meal, the family caught up on what was happening in each other's lives, including the boys' living arrangements at their uncle's place in Maiduguri as well as how they were progressing with their studies.

Next, Yakubu told the boys what life consisted of for him. His main job was going out with the village boys to cut firewood, using his old bow saw that he kept as sharp as a razor. He also cut wood for people who lived in other caves, especially for ladies who didn't have men in their group.

The family had planted vegetables in the hidden dells of the mountain, hoping against hope that Boko Haram wouldn't find them. They spent a lot of time bringing in wild yams and other tubers, leaves from various trees, and any other food they could find on the mountain. Whenever they could, they would catch and butcher the abandoned goats that wandered up onto the mountain. But Yakubu and the boys were careful not to go all the way into the valley. That was the women's job, and it was the women who brought the grain from their homes back in Chikide, as well as whatever else they could find.

After the meal, as usual, the conversation veered to the situation with Boko Haram. "Things are calm right now," Yakubu explained, "but I don't expect it to last. That's why I want you two boys to head back to Maiduguri tomorrow. I will have Godwin take you down to the main highway where you can catch a ride. It is just too dangerous for you to stay here for long."

Yakubu's rough face looked handsome in the lamplight. As Banner looked at him and listened to him talk, he loved him like never before. *I have a good dad! I have a wonderful dad!*

Though Banner wouldn't have admitted it, he was relieved to hear his father say that they should leave the next day. Though he loved being with the family, he was also afraid—especially later that night after his mother had shown them where to sleep and the lights went out. His dreams were full of Boko Haram terrorists who hauled him out of the cave and killed him.

Morning came as a relief. After sharing another simple meal of maize porridge, Yakubu gathered his family for a few last words. Turning to the two boys, he started speaking, his voice cracking with emotion. "Thanks for coming to visit us, and please be careful on your way out. And if we don't see each other again, let's not forget to always be faithful to the Lord we serve."

"Dad, you be careful as well," Bulus said, tears welling up in his eyes. "You are the one in the most danger. But God can protect you, I know."

Then Yakubu led in prayer. When the time came to part, not one eye was dry. Though it tore their hearts to say goodbye, Banner couldn't get out of that eerie cave fast enough. Not until they were crammed in a car on their way to Maiduguri could he relax. Even then, his mind continued to churn. *I wonder what will happen to my family—my father, my mother, and my three siblings. Oh God, please take care of them!*

Every Sunday morning Yakubu and his family joined over a hundred other Christians to worship God in their special meeting place. The open clearing lay snuggled between huge rock ramparts on three sides and had several massive trees around the edge to provide shade in the early morning hours. Flashy birds called mocking cliff chats flew from one rock rampart to the next, as if showing off their red, orange, and black colors. High up on the rock wall a baby rock hyrax appeared to be stressed, momentarily separated from his mother. Its funny bark pierced the morning quiet.

For the service, the people sat on the ground. Since it was rainy season, there was grass for the people to sit on. After yet another heartfelt worship service, the elders again gathered to discuss the future. For the past two Sundays, the watchmen had given their signal and the service had been interrupted. Fleeing for the caves had been the only logical thing to do.

It was now four months since Banner and Bulus had visited the family, and just as Yakubu had predicted, things had definitely taken a turn for the worse. The Boko Haram soldiers were furious that the villagers were surviving as well as they did on the mountain. Not only were they still alive, but they were worshipping every Sunday and were starting to raise their own food. Because their hiding places were so well concealed, they were difficult to find. Suddenly, routing out the Christians from the caves on the Mandara Mountains became a top priority for the terrorists.

"I think it's time we think of running for Cameroon," suggested one of the ministers. "Every day it is getting harder to hide from Boko Haram. We are losing too many people."

"And now they are throwing ground hot pepper into the caves and making us all cough," Yakubu said, shaking his head. "Our caves are becoming uninhabitable. I agree with the motion that we all form groups and flee as soon as we can."

"The worst thing is that some of the children are starving," interjected Esdras, Yakubu's brother-in-law. "We adults can more easily tighten our belts a notch, but when the children start dying, things are bad. I agree, let's run."

It was a solemn group of Christians who parted that day after the service. Everyone knew things had changed. And from that day on it was everyone for himself. There would be no more services on the mountain. The time had come to flee.

The very next week Boko Haram surrounded the mountain behind Chikide in their determination to get rid of the Christians. One thought kept coming to Yakubu: *Why didn't we leave a week ago when it was still relatively easy to escape to Cameroon? What can we do now?*

Yakubu talked to the people who hid in caves closest to them. Esdras, who was married to Yakubu's sister Doris, was in a group of twenty who had come up with a scheme to flee. Escaping was not going to be an easy feat, as their caves were only two thirds of the way up the mountain. They would have to climb to the top, then hike down the opposite flank toward Cameroon. And not until they hit the Cameroon flats would they be safe.

Yakubu and his family packed some food and their scant belongings and agreed to meet at midnight at the dell where they had their Sunday morning services. There was a half-moon sailing in the sky that night, so they agreed not to use flashlights once outside the caves. They would all be as quiet as possible as they sneaked their way out of Boko Haram's snare.

Everything went well until they crested the mountaintop. Feeling pretty confident that no Boko Haram soldiers were guarding the top, Yakubu decided they would simply walk across the open flat top and then head down the other side where he knew of a trail that led to Cameroon.

The group started across the flat top, single file, Yakubu taking the lead. Behind him came his wife and three children, with the rest of the group following behind.

The night was a lovely one. The sky was clear and surrounded with pale stars that resembled diamonds, and the moon hung like a luminous pearl above the group. Night birds sang their melancholy refrains. An assortment of fairylike breezes swept over the plain, playing with the travelers' hair and keeping them cool.

The group of refugees approached the forested edge of the plateau. Just as they were ready to drop onto a trail that wound steeply down the mountain, the bushes at the edge burst alive and four armed men jumped out. "Stop! Hands up!" The raucous voice ripped the silent night into a million splinters.

Shocked into total silence, the group had no option but to allow themselves to be caught. Yakubu's heart sank. *This is it. My day has come to die. What will happen to my family?*

"Where do you think you are going?" a Boko Haram soldier barked as he approached the group, who by now had their hands in the air.

"We were planning to go to Cameroon," Yakubu answered slowly. "But I guess we can't if you stop us."

"All of you get onto your knees," the fierce leader demanded. Then, motioning to Yakubu and Esdras, he led them over to the edge of the flat where the trail dropped off. "Kneel right here," the soldier instructed roughly. "You are going to pray the *Kalima Shahada.*"

The two men's hearts froze. They knew all too well what the *Kalima Shahada* was. It was the Muslims' last ritual prayer before death. The two men knelt in silence.

"If you pray the *Kalima Shahada,* you will go to heaven when you die," the Boko Haram warrior explained. "If you don't, you will burn in hell!"

"This is what you will pray," one of the other soldiers commanded.

"Inna lillahi wa inna ille irajiuna la villa ha illallahu. Allahu Akbar!"[1]

The two men were silent.

The Christians' silence enraged the terrorists. "If you don't pray this prayer, you are dead men!" the leader snarled. "I will kill you!"

Yakubu's answer was quiet, yet clear. "If I renounce Christ, I am already dead. If you must, go ahead and kill me."

Immediately two of the soldiers took action. It was over within a minute. They slaughtered them mercilessly.

Beside themselves with fury, one of the soldiers jerked Yakubu's bow saw out of his backpack and muttered, "Let's get rid of these infidel pigs." With the help of the others, they sawed the corpses of the two men into pieces, limb by limb.

Right where the trail dropped down toward Cameroon, off to the side a little, lay the first cave on the Cameroon side. It was a deep pit, like a kind of bottomless well. The four soldiers had been hiding right beside the cave when they ambushed the group of Christians. Now the leader remembered the well, and giving quick orders, they threw all the body pieces down into the well.

By now the children in the group were more than terrified. Naomi and Doris's hearts were bleeding and torn. Though they refused to lift their heads to watch the horrendous scene, they heard everything—even the thudding of the body pieces as they struck the walls of the cave.

The wicked deed done, the soldiers ordered the group to get up, take up their bags, and start marching. Back toward Chikide they went, into a terrible valley called The Unknown. There was no time to view or bury their dead. They had to march, and march they did. When they got to the valley, they were hauled in trucks to the Sambisa Forest.

———————————————

It was April 2015. The dry season was practically done with its job of drying up the now thirsty land, and the first threatening rumbles of impending thunderstorms could occasionally be heard on the horizon. The weather was swelteringly hot.

A huddle of women and children met in a courtyard under the spreading wings of a palm tree. It was midnight. "Is everything ready?" Naomi whispered, trying to see through the gloom. The new moon was covered with a bank of black clouds.

"I think so," her sister-in-law Doris answered, reaching out to touch the three children who crowded around. "I have the sack of food . . ."

"We have to be extremely careful," Naomi warned, her whisper barely audible. "We will travel in separate groups so if we get stopped by any Boko Haram soldiers, they won't get all of us. I think I will go first with the children. Then you can come fifteen minutes later with the sack of food."

"I would rather you carry the food," Doris suggested quietly. "You are so much stronger. Then I will come behind with the children."

"Okay, are you all ready?" Naomi asked again.

After the terrible night of the execution, the group had spent a year and a half in the Sambisa Forest. Naomi and Doris and the three children were Boko Haram's slaves. Life was terrible for all of them, but especially for Naomi because she did not try to hide her faith.

The soldiers normally kept Naomi and the children locked in a building from early evening till the next morning, knowing they would escape if they could. She was forced to work hard all day. Often they insulted her, calling her an infidel and a "Christian dog." They beat her to try to make her wear a hijab. But like her husband, she stood firm and suffered for Christ's sake. Just recently, however, the soldiers had loosened their grip somewhat, and Naomi and the children were no longer locked up at night.

Suzanna was just turning sixteen, which was the main reason Naomi knew it was high time to plan their escape. Any day Boko Haram might force Suzanna to marry one of their soldiers.

Habila was fourteen and little Markus was twelve. They were still too young to be trained as warriors, but they were slowly being brainwashed by Islamic indoctrination. That was another reason Naomi wanted to get her family out of the Sambisa Forest. She couldn't stand the possibility of them becoming Boko Haram warriors.

The rest of the original group had been separated from Naomi and her sister-in-law Doris as soon as they had arrived at the Sambisa Forest. Since none of Doris's children were with her anymore, she was willing to help Naomi escape with hers.

God help us! Naomi cried inwardly. And then, giving her children a quick hug and some fresh instructions, she took up her sack of food and disappeared into the dark night. Sprinting toward the end of the courtyard, Naomi knew what she needed to do. They had made their preparations the afternoon before, setting up bricks on both sides of the low wall so they could cross. After she flung the sack across the wall, she climbed over it, landing on the other side.

Quietly she left the village toward the south. Taking a trail she was familiar with, she remembered what they had agreed on. *We will meet under the baobab tree a mile south of the village.* It wasn't long till Naomi arrived. Dropping her sack, she sat at the base of the tree, the trunk between her and her enemies. While she waited, she planned.

Naomi knew they would have to walk for days before they were out of Boko Haram territory. During that time, it would be crucial to avoid towns at all costs, because the towns close to the Sambisa Forest had been cooperating with Boko Haram. Then, once they got to a larger town, they would seek help. Naomi assessed their sack of food, hoping desperately it would keep them alive until they got out.

Fifteen minutes went by fast, and still Doris and the children didn't show up. *It's just that children walk slower than I do,* Naomi consoled herself.

After half an hour had passed, Naomi's blood turned cold. *Why, oh why, did I agree to bring the food instead of my children?*

Slowly two more hours dragged by. The pain in Naomi's heart grew almost unbearable. Finally she started her trek to freedom alone, weeping as she walked. *There is no way I will go back to Boko Haram. Not even my children would want me to do that. The soldiers would kill me for sure. Oh, I wonder what happened to Doris and my precious children! Surely Doris will plan another escape and they will eventually be safe.*

When Naomi safely arrived in Maiduguri, she found Bulus and three of the other boys at the house of her husband's brother. Banner, she discovered, had been accepted at Favoured Sisters Christian Foundation[2] in Jos, where he was receiving good care and a decent education. She decided to rent a small house and stay in Maiduguri for the time being.

As soon as she could, Naomi traveled to Jos and visited Banner at the school. They spent hours telling each other everything that had happened since Banner had spent that memorable night in the cave with his family. They both wept as Naomi told the story of Yakubu's death, her terrible ordeal in the Sambisa Forest, and how the three youngest children were still back there.

"One thing comforts me every day about your father's passing," Naomi sobbed. "When I heard him witness to those wicked men, I knew this was going to be the end for him. I knew that within a few short minutes he would be with Jesus, and I am sure that's where he is now!"

"Amen!" Banner sniffled. "And Mama, it would probably have been easier for you if they had taken your life as well. I can hardly stand what you have had to suffer."

"I have thought of that a thousand times, son. But I always end up thanking God that He kept me here for the sake of you children. I still think the other three children will be free someday. When they come back, they will need me. Especially little Markus."

"Mama, I want to tell you how thankful I am that I can be here at

---

[2] Favoured Sisters Christian Foundation is an orphanage and school that takes in children and youth who have lost one or both of their parents.

this orphanage. It's a godly place. Not only am I getting a good education, but I am also learning ways to make my living once my studies are finished."

Naomi nodded, tears of gratitude gleaming in her eyes.

"Here I have a daddy again." Banner stopped, overcome with emotion. "Our teacher, Amos, is like a daddy to all of us. He teaches us to know God. He teaches us to pray and to read the Bible. My Christian life is growing by leaps and bounds since I am here. I can't help it; I love this place."

"Praise the Lord!" Naomi gushed, a smile peeping through her tears. "I am so glad to hear that! Your daddy would be so happy to hear that you are growing in your Christian life. That was always his vision for you boys."

"I feel so unworthy," Banner said, smiling through his tears. "How is it that I have a special place like this to live? None of the other children do."

"It's a miracle," Naomi sighed. "A blessing from God Almighty."

"And guess what Amos is dreaming for us, Mama. He wants us to become missionaries! Sometimes I can't sleep at night, thinking about being a missionary to our friends in Chikide. Do you think that might happen someday?"

"Absolutely!" Naomi exclaimed. "And if that happens, I have a feeling your daddy would know and be so proud of you!"

"But for right now, Banner, we have an important job ahead of us. Though we don't have any clue what's happening to Suzanna, Habila, and Markus, we need to pray for them every day."

"Yes, Mama, I will do that until we hear they have escaped, or have been rescued. I'll do that till the day I die!"

Photos and Author's Notes

Under the Tamarind Tree

Most of the information for this chapter came from Mary Ann Moyer Kulp's book *No Longer Strangers.* One of the highlights of the trip to Garkida was to see this immense tree, now more than a hundred years old, where the first Church of the Brethren services were held. To actually see and touch the natural stone pulpit where Stover preached his first messages and to read the inscription on the plaque seemed almost like a sacred experience.

A natural stone pulpit stands under the tree just as it did almost a hundred years ago. Only now the pulpit wears a metal plaque and is fenced in for protection.

Tumba

When we first started our interview, Tumba seemed almost unwilling to talk about his experiences. But once we sat down and Joshua talked to him in Hausa, explaining the purpose of the book, Tumba warmed up.

My admiration for him soared when he told me how he had denied Christ when Gambo didn't. His face was totally transparent when he bluntly told me, "I renounced Christ." He didn't try to hide the truth.

Tumba showed little emotion when he told me about his wife and two children. Though he didn't shed a tear, his eyes showed the pain clearly. Our hearts reached out and bonded with this young man and his suffering.

"Where are your wife and children now?" I asked hesitantly.

"I have no idea," was his sad answer.

"Do you resent the Boko Haram for having done all this to you?"

The rocky hills that Tumba Tizhe lives in.

"No, I have forgiven them. I just thank God that I was able to come back home to be with my family and my church."

Tumba's hands are scarred for life. He has no feeling in them but can use them to work.

The Dazzling Curtain

A number of ladies joined us at a table the evening we heard Rebeca Ishaku's story. Almost all of their husbands had been killed by Boko Haram. Our hearts warmed toward them as they told us their stories.

Rebeca Ishaku and Euni, the author's wife.

Chibok Girls

After the 109 girls were released, the Nigerian government whisked them off to Abuja for their safety. They are taking good care of them and giving them the best education that Nigeria can offer. For that reason it was not possible for me to meet with any of them.

Some EYN pastors, however, arranged a visit with five of the girls' relatives and one of the girls who had jumped off the truck that first night. I interviewed them as a group instead of individually. They seemed bashful at first, almost as if afraid to pour out their stories. After I told them that the purpose of the book was to encourage other Christians, and that I would not write anything they wanted me to keep private, the stories started to pour out.

Salomi, one of the brave girls who had jumped from the truck, gave a first-hand account of how Boko Haram had pounced upon the school that fateful night, and how the girls had been kidnapped and hauled away. Her eyes filled with tears as she told us how she thanked God for deliverance, and how she prayed for her companions who were still missing.

Philip didn't show much emotion as he told me the story of his sister Margaret, but it was easy to sense the great love and respect he had for her.

It didn't take me long to understand what an important role Margaret played during the Chibok kidnapping. She was as bold as a lion and became

A joyous meal shared with the Chibok folks after the interviews were over.

the undisputed leader of the girls, especially of the eighteen who refused to renounce Christ.

Hanatu, Yagana's mother, was the next person to be interviewed. Yagana was eighteen at the time of the kidnapping. She was the first to jump from the truck. Hanatu told me how Yagana's bold example paved the way for several other girls to follow suit.

Philimon Adamu spoke about his sister Naomi, who was kidnapped when she was twenty years old. In his description, I was able to get a glimpse of his feisty little sister whom Boko Haram couldn't crush.

Though most of the other girls' diaries were confiscated, Naomi carried hers with her when she was released, after three years of captivity.

Marymu was the mother of Lylian, who was kidnapped at seventeen years of age. The saddest part of her story was that her daughter had been married off to a Boko Haram soldier and was still held in captivity.

Yanaf, Rifkatu's mother, half told, half wept as she told us her sad story. After the girls were kidnapped, Yanaf was chosen to be part of a commission from Chibok to help get the girls back.

When the first twenty-one girls were released, and later the eighty-eight, Yanaf was part of the group that went to meet them. Both times Yanaf searched the crowd for her precious daughter, but both times to no avail.

At this writing, Rifkatu remains a prisoner of Boko Haram, and Yanaf is still waiting and praying for the time when she can once again see her daughter.

A photo of Naomi's diary that came out in the news.

Already Dead

Banner Yakubu's story was one of the saddest stories I had heard, and I had heard plenty. Banner's eyes shone. Although the Boko Haram terrorists had slaughtered his dear father, Yakubu, the man he loved most, Banner felt no rancor toward them. At the time of the interview, Boko Haram still held three of his brothers and sisters captive, but he did not hate them. His genuine smile told me he had forgiven them.

Sitting beside Banner sat Amos Dibal, who, along with two ladies, had dedicated their lives to taking care of orphans from the Boko Haram crisis. Their orphanage, Favoured Sisters Christian Foundation, is located on the outskirts of Jos. The faith Amos showed in his face now radiated from his students, who loved him and followed his example. Under Amos's influence, Banner had not only forgiven Boko Haram but had decided to become a missionary to his people when he had finished his schooling.

Banner Yakubu. His face shone
with the joy of the Lord.

Sunday Comes Home on Friday

I stared in wonder at the large emotionless woman in front of me. "Did you say your son Sunday came home today?" I asked incredulously, shaking my head. "Not this today!"

The lady nodded, a hint of a smile on her face. "Yes, and I am so happy."

"Where was he all this time?" I probed, still doubting.

"He was in Cameroon in the refugee camp. I scratched together enough money to send for him, and he and his half-brother came home today."

I hated being a doubting Thomas, but as Sunday stepped forward and joined us, I asked him, "Did you really just come back from the refugee camp today?"

"I sure did!" he replied with a big smile. "After being gone for four years!"

Liyatu and her son, Sunday, who came home on Friday.

There Is a God!

In spite of her suffering, Asabe still wears her smile.

Asabe Daniel's story was long and sad. She is a strong woman who has been hardened by all the suffering she has faced. But her emotions spilled out in tears when she told us how the soldiers had beaten her, and how she had been sure she was going to die that day.

Why she involuntarily cried out, "There is a God!" in that moment of crisis still amazes her. Her words probably still haunt the Boko Haram terrorist who beat her.

Ladi

Margaret Bitrus was one of the several dozen people from Gwoza who waited under the mango tree for the opportunity to tell their stories that hot Friday. All the stories we gleaned that day were sad and yet triumphant,

Margaret Bitrus, the tough mother who had her baby in a cave.

but I knew I couldn't include them all in this book. But after Margaret shared her story, I looked at my wife and sighed, "This story I want to share. Can you imagine—a baby born in a cave?"

We couldn't meet little Ladi the day I interviewed Margaret, as her father had taken her to the city for a doctor's appointment. But it was special to have the opportunity to meet the brave mother.

Pumpum "Orphans"

The slender 15-year-old girl sat on the doorstep beside Joshua, my translator for the day. Abigail Madu's fascinating story kept us spellbound for an hour as she told us the saga of her captivity and then their liberation from Boko Haram.

It was hard to imagine what this gentle girl had been through when she and her two siblings had been kidnapped by Boko Haram, and how at the age of twelve she took good care of her siblings. My admiration for her soared as the story continued.

Abigail seemed like such a brave, gentle young lady. Only once did she break down and shed some tears.

When I heard about the way they treated little Jonathan, I asked if he was in the swarm of children around us.

Abigail nodded, then called out in her quiet voice, "Monday and Jonathan, come."

The children came, timidly. They were even more bashful than their big sister. I talked to them briefly, but all I could get out of them were stares and feeble smiles.

Abigail's mother had gone to town on an errand the day of the interview, so she is missing from the photo.

At the time of the interview, it was still not safe for Abigail's family to move back to their Pumpum home. They were staying at the refugee camp in Kwarhi where they were safe and well provided for.

Left to right: Monday, Madu, Jonathan, and Abigail.

An Ant-Infested Prayer Chamber

Thirty-year-old Hajaratu Yohanna was a teacher in EYN's John Guli Bible College on the outskirts of Michika. She readily told us her story of how Boko Haram raided, looted, and burned the college compound that fatal Sunday morning. She chuckled when she told us about the hours she spent feeding herself to the ants.

"I was so sick," she exclaimed, smiling broadly at my wife and me, "and so afraid to get up. So I just let the ants have their will and way with me."

Hajaratu's smile was heartwarming.

Saratu's Turkey Gobbler

Asiburyu, Joshua's adopted sister, crushing baobab leaves for draw soup.

Joshua Ishaya was not only a wonderful translator, he also became our close friend during the time we traveled together in northeast Nigeria. Joshua and Chinna, our other translator, both translated many stories to us from their native Hausa language.

Once Joshua even took me to his home for a delicious meal of draw soup.

While I visited Joshua's home and

experienced the draw soup, I interviewed Saratu, Joshua's mother. Joshua had told me earlier that she had a story to tell me about her turkey gobbler.

With many a smile and a few gestures, it didn't take Saratu long to tell me the story of how the turkey had saved her life that dreadful morning of the Boko Haram crisis.

Saratu, Joshua, and Ishaya.

Mealtime for the chickens.

Mercy and Peace

I knew Godia was blind and partially deaf due to having polio when she was young, but I didn't fully realize the extent of her handicap until I began our interview.

"How old are you?" I asked Godia. Her blank stare told me she hadn't understood a thing. And Mary, her daughter, hadn't understood either.

Joshua then asked the question in Hausa, and Mary shouted the question into Godia's ear.

Only then did Godia respond.

What surprised me most during the interview with her was how she rejoiced despite her difficulty. She rejoiced because she had a daughter who was willing to yell into her ear. She rejoiced because Christian Aid Ministries had given her a house. She rejoiced because God had delivered them when she and her children were such easy prey for Boko Haram.

Godia smiling as she counts her blessings!

The most remarkable moment came when Godia said how glad she was that God had taken Paul home when He did. "Because that way he was there to receive Little Peace when she got to heaven. Can you imagine the joy for them both as Paul welcomed her home and then held her on his lap?"

A Deep, Deep Sleep!

The dangerous place where the boys crossed the road.
They crossed from the opposite side.

Mr. Quickly

Carl Shankster was born in Garkida, Nigeria, and lived there for the first eighteen years of his life.

My introductory interview with Carl had been an important part of the preparation for my trip to Nigeria. He had eighteen years of firsthand experience of living in Garkida and told us many interesting Nigerian stories, some of which found their way onto the pages of this book.

Though Carl and his family were part of the Church of the Brethren in Garkida, in later years they joined the German Baptist Church and now live in Silver Lake, Indiana.

One of the over two thousand wells that Mr. Quickly engineered.

Patience

During our interview with Patience, her brother Dawi's wife didn't join us because it was still too hard for her to speak about the things that had happened. Patience's brave mother, Mwada, however, did join us.

Dawi had warned me before the interview that his mother was still traumatized by the tragedy and found it hard to talk about it. I promised to be careful and began by explaining the purpose of the book. I explained that their testimony would be read by thousands who could then take courage from God's presence in their tragedy.

Patience fascinated me as she poured out the story so sincerely and so clearly. They had been such a happy family. There had been so much joy, so much love. Mwada's face, however, remained expressionless, and I began to sense how much she had lost.

As Patience was describing the awful things that had happened the night of the attack, Mwada suddenly jumped up and fled from the room. My wife followed her and found her in the bedroom, lying on the bed, weeping her heart out. My wife hugged her and prayed for her.

After she told the story of the Boko Haram crisis, I thought Patience was finished. But there was another sad chapter in her life. Soon after the raid, she had gotten married. Then, after they had one baby and another on the way, her husband died of sickness. I marveled at her strength, her endurance, and yes, her patience!

At the end, the family told us how they had forgiven Boko Haram and told us of all their blessings despite their loss.

"At least we know one thing,"

Mala, who has Down syndrome, and the author.

Mwada said, now composed and relaxed. "Thomas, Ibrahim, and Arhyel are in heaven with Jesus."

As my wife and I laid our hands on Mwada and prayed, I begged God for comfort for this dear sister who had suffered so much.

Euni's heart bonded with Mwada's as she comforted her.

Patience, with her brother Dawi, on whom she depends for so many of her needs.

The Hug of Death

After a lively Sunday morning worship service at Favoured Sisters Christian Foundation and a tour of the premises, my wife and I found ourselves in Amos Dibal's office. For a big part of the afternoon, Amos called in orphans who told us their sad stories.

In the same office where I had interviewed Banner an hour earlier, Shadrach and Esther timidly told me their story of how their mother was blown up by a suicide bomber. They were both overwhelmed by the kindness of Amos and Mary, the director and the matron of the orphanage. They were so grateful. Here they had each other, they had the opportunity to study, and they had plenty of food. Above all, they were living in a place where they could learn to know God.

Shadrach and Esther, two years after their Boko Haram crisis.

Note to readers: Pray for the Christians in Nigeria. As this book goes to press in August 2020, the persecution is worsening, with Christians being attacked by both Boko Haram and Fulani herdsmen. In this year alone, over 1400 Christians have been killed in Nigeria.

Chapter 6

Sunday Comes Home on Friday

The stampede was chaotic that dark, horrendous evening in October 2014. As the sound of gunfire enveloped the village of Gava just east of the city of Gwoza, the people fled with the awful screams of *"Allahu Akbar!"* ringing in their ears. As was typical with Boko Haram raids, the next sight was that of their houses and their chapel going up in flames. Everyone ran in terror.

Liyatu Ibrahim ran with the rest, clinging to the hand of Hannah, the youngest of her children—the only child she had managed to find. As all the Gwoza folks had learned, the only thing to do when Boko Haram hit was to run due east, toward the Mandara Mountain range. The only safe place was some dark cave to hide in, and the Mandara Mountains had plenty of those.

Liyatu ran, hoping against hope not to meet up with any Boko Haram soldiers. As she ran, her thoughts went all directions. *Where is my husband? Where are the rest of my children? What will happen to us? Will we ever find each other again?*

That night Liyatu and little Hannah slept in a cave with some friends. Sick with worry about her other children and her husband, she slept little, but at least she was able to rest.

The next day was a rough one for all the Gava villagers. Many, like Liyatu, spent the whole day climbing up into the mountains, looking for their families. But Liyatu didn't find a trace of her loved ones. Someone suggested that maybe they were following others over the top of the mountain and down the other side toward the refugee camp in Cameroon.

That evening when Liyatu came back to the cave where she had slept the night before, her friends told her their sad experiences from the day. "Some of us women sneaked back to town to look for the dead and hunt for food," one lady told Liyatu. "But no men were there," she continued. "And I can understand why . . ."

Liyatu knew one reason—the Boko Haram were much harsher with the men than the women. Also, the men were up on the mountain hiding and looking for suitable caves. But she suspected the lady had other reasons for saying what she did. "W-what did you find in the village?" Liyatu stammered.

"It was horrible," the neighbor answered, her eyes showing her pain and hesitation to tell Liyatu the truth. "I have sad news for you."

"What happened?" Liyatu pressed. "Don't hide anything from me. I am prepared for the worst."

"There were twenty-five villagers killed, and your father was one of them. We ladies had to bury the dead because there were no men around."

"Oh, no!" Liyatu wept, burying her face in her hands. "They killed my father. I am sure it was because he refused to renounce Christ. Praise the Lord, he was faithful till the end . . ."

"We can be sure he is in heaven," the neighbor echoed. "That is something to be thankful for."

Meanwhile Liyatu's husband Ibrahim and the rest of the children had topped the mountain and were heading down the other side as fast as they could toward Cameroon.

As the group approached an immense refugee camp in Cameroon, thirteen-year-old Sunday and his half-brother Emmanuel somehow got separated from the rest of the family. On their own now, they followed the multitude into the camp, while Ibrahim and the rest of the children followed a smaller group that decided to avoid the camp. They kept on traveling, swerving south, then west, and finally back into Madagali, Nigeria—one of the few places in this part of Nigeria that wasn't controlled by Boko Haram.

Liyatu spent a week on the mountain with her little daughter, hoping to find her husband and children. When they didn't show up, she traveled on south to safer lands in Cameroon. Though she didn't know it, her husband had traveled the same path earlier.

Like her husband and many others, Liyatu feared the refugee camp in Cameroon. Rumors about the horrid life there abounded.

When Liyatu reached Madagali, she was glad to find a safe place where the EYN church was taking care of refugees. There, to her great joy, she found Ibrahim and two of their children. But her happiness was tempered by the sad news that Sunday and Emmanuel were not with them. Supposedly they were in the refugee camp, but no one knew for sure. What she did not know is that this would haunt her heart for years to come.

Sunday and Emmanuel topped a low hill and gazed down on what looked like a white ocean floating in an immense flat. *It looks like a city,* Sunday mused wonderingly. *And I guess it is. A city of white tents. I wonder what life will be like in a refugee camp.*

He looked back up the road to see if his family was following, but all he could see was several dozen fellow refugees who surrounded them, staring, like him, at the valley full of white tents.

After staring for several minutes, the trekkers started up again, walking hesitantly toward the unknown. Soon they would be in a camp with more than 40,000 refugees from northeast Nigeria. That number was growing. Everywhere, people were running away from Boko Haram.

As Sunday and his friends entered the white, canvas-filled city, they were ushered into a large tent that was obviously the headquarters. Their life had changed dramatically from a quiet little town called Gava to being surrounded at all times by hordes of people in a place where silence and solitude were unknown.

The first thing Sunday and Emmanuel faced in the building was something they had to live with for the next four years—the disdain of the Cameroonians. "What are your names, and where are you from?" a tall man snapped from where he was sitting behind a simple table. "And where is your family?"

For the next fifteen minutes Sunday and Emmanuel were questioned and drilled by a man who wore a continual sneer. His body language and manner left only one message—*I am sick and tired of you Nigerians who keep coming over the mountain to bother us Cameroonians.*

Sunday was worried sick about his family. *Where is my father? How can I face this situation without him? Oh, how I miss my mother!*

Emmanuel was almost crying. A year younger than Sunday, he was quiet by nature. Sunday could see that behind his expressionless face, he was in even worse shape emotionally than he himself was. *Poor Emmanuel,* Sunday sighed. *If I miss my family, how much more does he!*

Suddenly tears welled up in Sunday's eyes, and he felt like screaming at the tall official. Did he think they had come to Cameroon for a picnic? Did he think they preferred this noisy, hot place to their own home? *You are mistaken, man! We hate to be here worse than you do. But Boko Haram makes us willing to abandon the comfort of our homes to come face your scowling airs!*

Fortunately for Sunday and Emmanuel, they had traveled to Cameroon with a neighboring family whom they knew well. Since the rest of Sunday's family never showed up, this family promptly took them in. The officials showed them a large white tent that already seemed full of refugees. One corner of the tent was curtained off, and that was to be home for the family and the two boys.

Sunday and Emmanuel and their adoptive family soon learned the tricks to the trade of being refugees in Cameroon. Though it was a tremendous battle to survive in the difficult circumstances, they soon discovered it was either learn or die.

The most important element for surviving in the camp was getting your share of food. Once a week the distribution trucks drove up to the headquarters and parked. Sunday and Emmanuel were among the boys who detected the truck's arrival first. Their keen ears heard the first rumble of the trucks, and then their nimble feet took wings. Usually they were able to get near the front of the long lines. Then, pushing and conniving like all the rest, they managed to get their share of food before most of the others.

Not that there wasn't enough food for everybody; you just didn't have to stand in line as long. Standing in the hot sun for hours was not a favorite pastime for any refugee.

The trucks brought in rice or soybeans, and sometimes guinea corn or maize. The assortment also included cooking oil, salt, and other basics.

The camp provided the basic pots to cook up a meal. The men collected firewood from the surrounding bush, while the ladies did the cooking on triangles of rocks on the ground.

The ladies hauled the water from several wells scattered throughout the camp. And since the boys didn't have much else to do, the ladies often got them to help.

The boys also discovered the play areas where young people met to socialize and play games. Various classes took place inside the big white tents so the youth wouldn't miss out in their schooling.

Besides missing their family, what was hardest for Sunday and Emmanuel in the refugee camp was the lack of privacy. There were always people swarming all over. Since their allotted portion of the big white tent was so small, they only went there to sleep. Otherwise they spent their time working or socializing with other youth. Often they just sat around doing nothing, and that was the most boring thing of all.

As always happens in situations like this, tension hung in the air and fights flared up often—fights between children, fights among youth, fights among families, and especially fights between the refugees and the Cameroonians.

Although the Cameroonians' disdain was a hard pill to swallow, the white people who brought food and visited the camp regularly were always friendly. As friendly, it seemed, as the Cameroonians were spiteful.

Another thing that bothered the refugees was the rumors of embezzled funds. Word spread that a lot of the money people sent for the refugees somehow found its way into the pockets of the leaders of the camp and other government officials. This made the refugees growl, especially when their stomachs were already growling for lack of good food.

During the time when Sunday and Emmanuel were in the refugee camp in Cameroon, they often dreamed of escaping and going home. This seemed impossible because they were far from any safe cities and had no idea how to get to them.

Also, the boys knew that the refugees had to have a permit to return to Nigeria. If you didn't have one, the tight surveillance around the camp would catch you. The refugee camp directors only gave permits to those who could cough up enough money to get to the big Nigerian cities to the south. Cameroon was determined not to have their country infested by Nigerians.

Sunday and Emmanuel had no way to make any money. The camp simply did not provide any opportunity for earning money. Barring a miracle, the two boys were stuck there, just like the thousands of other refugees who milled around the camp.

Days dragged into weeks, weeks into months, and months into years. Time went by slowly in the sweltering canvas-filled city. In the end, Sunday and Emmanuel lived in the refugee camp for four long years.

One day a man whom they knew from Gava showed up and called them aside. "Your mother sent money so you can go home," he announced, reaching into his pocket. "She sent 12,000 naira[1] for your bus fares. You need to go to the headquarters and show the money so they'll give you a permit to leave camp. Then we'll catch a bus to Mubi tomorrow. Your mother will meet us there."

Sunday and Emmanuel were shocked. Could this be true?

The two excited boys rushed to the headquarters with their benefactor. After answering a lot of questions and filling out the necessary papers, the two boys had their permits to leave the camp the next morning. Sunday could hardly sleep that night. The next day would be Friday. *Is it possible that tomorrow I will see my family?*

The next morning, Friday morning, Sunday and Emmanuel got up early to leave. They said goodbye to the family who had so graciously taken them in, then caught the bus for Mubi. It was a little before noon when the bus slammed to a stop and the three got off. Overjoyed, Sunday saw that his mother and father were there to receive them. With tears of joy they embraced each other.

The market where the bus unloaded its passengers was hot, and people milled all around, but for Liyatu the world stopped. It was a day she had long dreamed of and prayed for. Soon the little cluster of people were talking a mile a minute, trying their best to catch up with all that had happened during those four long years. It was as if the people and the market didn't exist. The family was together again!

---

[1] Around US$35.

Chapter 7

There Is a God!

*T*he evening was chaotic but happy. Nine children and their parents crowded around two big pots of food placed strategically on a large mat on the floor in the middle of the room. A single bulb dangled from the ceiling, giving just enough light for the family to see the upcoming meal. One pot was brimming with plain white rice, the other with beans.

Everybody helped themselves as best as they could to the contents in both pots. Then, finding a corner where they could eat comfortably, they fell to, their fingers serving as a spoon. "Not so fast!" Daniel Zufka, the father of the tribe, ordered in his quiet voice. "Take it easy. There is plenty for everybody."

Asabe, Daniel's wife, was an outgoing woman, as outgoing as Daniel was gentle and quiet. But the two got along and the children knew their limits.

Though the atmosphere was loud and rambunctious, it always made

137

Asabe feel good to see her children well fed and happy. *We are anything but rich*, she sighed, filling her own plate last. But because they served God and her husband was a hard worker, they always had enough to eat. And in that sense, they were rich.

At that moment the peaceful evening was shattered. Asabe and her husband and the bigger children immediately knew what was happening.

"Allahu Akbar! Allahu Akbar! Allahu Akbar!" were the shouts that interrupted the evening meal that fateful night in November 2014. As the noise increased, so did the terror.

Next it was gunfire. *Puk-a-puk-a-puk-a-puk-a,* an AK-47 rifle spat out in quick succession. It was a sound that northeast Nigeria was hearing more and more. And along with it came the cry, "Run! Run for the mountains. Run for your lives!"

Running was not easy for Asabe and her husband. The sizes of their nine children descended in perfect increments, like pipes on an organ. Grabbing the baby, Asabe looked at Daniel, her eyes big in horror. "Let's run!" she cried.

Daniel picked up the next to the smallest, told the rest to follow, and then ran as well. Their supper was forgotten. Everybody knew where to run.

It was a horrible night for everybody in Gava. Most of the population was Christian, so Boko Haram burned almost every house to the ground. Two chapels were incinerated, and stores were looted and burned as well. In one evening, the whole town was basically destroyed.

Worst of all, the terrorists were learning that if they came into a village merely yelling their war cry, the people almost always escaped. So this time they circled the village first and stationed soldiers at strategic spots around the village. As the villagers tried to escape, the *puk-a-puk-a-puk-a-puk-a* of AK-47s came from all directions. The death toll that evening came to a staggering 133.

Daniel knew the Mandara Mountains like the palm of his hand, and it didn't take him long to decide where to take his family. Toward the top of the mountain, far off the beaten trail, was a large cave. It took the family several hours to hike up to the cave, because they stopped often to rest and watch with horror the red-gold colors that swirled into the night sky as the fires lapped up the village. It was a sad family that finally entered the cave's narrow entrance and bedded down at midnight.

The next day was a low point for the people of Gava. Many of them went to the valley to find their dead and give them a decent burial. Fortunately, the Boko Haram soldiers had not stayed around. There was nothing left anyway, so the warring soldiers had hustled back to Gwoza, which was fast becoming their local headquarters. Full of fear and dread, the villagers sneaked down into the valley to do what they had to do.

Soon after arriving, Asabe was devastated when she and Daniel found her father's body lying out in the hot sun.

Like everyone else who fled to the Mandara Mountains, Daniel and Asabe's family learned to cope. For a month everyone pitched in to make life go on, even if it was filled with hardships. At least their immediate family was accounted for and alive. During the first month of living in the cave, slipping down to the village every day wasn't too dangerous. Boko Haram did not seem interested in their town—or what was left of it. Asabe accompanied several other ladies to the village daily to look for any food that hadn't been burned and to harvest their crops in the surrounding fields.

Early one morning Asabe headed to the village again, looking for food. She also wanted to pick up several things in their house, which, surprisingly, was still standing. As usual, she didn't take her children along.

Asabe and Daniel were among the fortunate few whose house hadn't been burned to the ground. When Asabe opened the door of their now empty home, she was shocked to find two soldiers sorting through the few things she still had stored there.

There was no time to run. The soldier closest to her raised his gun immediately and ordered her into the house. Asabe obeyed, trembling from head to foot.

"What do you want, you infidel pig?" the soldier snarled. "Why don't you stay up on your precious mountain where you are safe?"

Falling to her knees, Asabe explained, "My family is hungry, so I thought I might be able to find some food."

"There is no food here," the soldier barked. "And I am hungry too. We are all hungry."

"Will you renounce Christ?" the other soldier inserted, frowning a deep frown. "Islam is the real religion."

Asabe shook her head. "I can't renounce Christ! What evil has He ever done to me? He is my only salvation!"

This clear answer made the soldier angry. With one huge kick, he sent Asabe sprawling. *"Allahu Akbar!"* he exclaimed, jerking a sword from his belt.

Then, bending over the prostrate woman, he held the sword to her throat. "Will you renounce Christ now?"

This time Asabe only shook her head. But that was more than enough to ignite the wicked soldier's fury. Replacing the sword and raising the gun, he brought the stock down squarely onto the poor woman cowering on the ground at his feet. *"Allahu Akbar!"*

By then Asabe was sure the soldiers were going to kill her. Her heart was filled with terror. All she could think of was to say, "There is a God!" over and over again.

Every time Asabe said, "There is a God!" the soldier cursed and slammed the butt of his gun down upon her body mercilessly. The soldier didn't care where or how. He just used the gun to give her the worst beating she had ever experienced.

"There is a God!"

Wham! Wham! Wham!

"I can't take it anymore!" Asabe screamed. "Please don't kill me here!

No one will find me in this deserted house. If you kill me, take me where people can find me and give me a decent burial."

Once the soldier was tired from beating Asabe, he stopped and ordered her to get up. "You are coming with us!" he shouted.

Asabe's body screamed in pain and blood oozed from her bruises, but she slowly got up. "March!" the soldier commanded heartlessly. "Go!" With a final kick he sent her stumbling out the door.

The two soldiers escorted Asabe to the plaza in the center of the village. To her surprise, about thirty other people were there, most of them Asabe's neighbors. Some of them had been captured up on the mountain, but others had been trapped in the valley, much like Asabe.

There were several older men and women in the group, and Asabe's heart melted for them. There were also about a dozen children standing in the circle, their eyes wide in terror.

Soon the captives were all loaded onto a big truck like cattle. As they roared down the dirt country roads, Asabe realized, *We are heading for the dreaded Sambisa Forest.* All she could do was pray, so pray she did. God was more than willing to listen and answer the suffering woman's sincere prayer, but poor Asabe had no way of knowing how or when He would answer.

Hours later, the truck slammed to a stop at another village plaza. The captives were unloaded and told to stand in the center of the plaza. In the distance Asabe could see other captives peering out from behind the trees that flanked the plaza.

Under a huge tamarind tree in a wicker chair sat Boko Haram's leader, Abubakar, in all his grandeur. The lead soldier approached Abubakar and announced, "Well, Master, we did what you told us to do. There they are."

Staring at the captives in the plaza, Abubakar ignored the soldier. Suddenly he got up and walked over to inspect them more closely. Then, turning to the soldier, he sneered, "These are all way too old. Why do you bring me trash? I don't want this cargo!"

Asabe could see that the truck driver was afraid. There was no telling what his angry master might do to him.

"What shall I do?" the soldier croaked. "I brought them . . . Shall I take them back?"

"I don't care what you do with them!" Abubakar shouted, turning on his heel and heading back to his throne. "Just don't bring trash like this. You know better than that. Take them and get rid of them!"

Since it was late and the sun was already going down, the captives were locked into a large building. Several guards watched them all night long.

The next day the captives were loaded back onto the truck and they retraced their tracks. As soon as they got outside the area controlled by Boko Haram, the soldiers stopped and unloaded their "trash." Fortunately, they were close to a main highway.

The refugees scraped together enough money to take public transportation to Maiduguri where most of them had relatives. After they were on the way, Asabe settled down in a corner of the truck's bed. As the whine of the tires on the pavement helped block out all other noises, she reflected on her situation. *Oh, I feel sick,* she moaned, clutching her head in her hands. *I have a fever and I ache all over.* She realized her sickness was a result of the terrible beating she had received from the merciless soldier the day before, and she prayed that God would have mercy on the poor man's soul.

I am hungry and thirsty, Asabe moaned inwardly. *But soon, very soon, I will be at my sister's place, and she will take care of me. She will feed me and put salve on my wounds. I will be fine until I can get back together with my family.*

As she pondered her situation, she began rejoicing and her mood changed. *Oh, how can I thank God enough for saving me? At least I am not in the Sambisa Forest, a slave to some Boko Haram beast, like so many of my sisters in Christ. I am so fortunate to be among elderly refugees so*

Abubakar would despise us. He is mean to call us trash, but now I understand. It is a tremendous blessing to be his scum.

Suddenly Asabe remembered her murdered father, lying on the ground in the hot Nigerian sun. *At least he was ready to go,* she sobbed into her hands, her shoulders shaking. She had no doubt that her father had gone to be with Jesus. The people who refused to renounce Christ were the ones Boko Haram slaughtered. And they were the ones Jesus received in heaven, the ones He gave the crown of life! Yes, she decided, her father was well off.

Then, controlling her emotions, Asabe started imagining that she was telling her family about her experiences. She imagined the cave, lit up with candles and their old tin lamp. The children huddled around, staring at her intently, all ears. Daniel's love and admiration for her shone from his eyes. As she remembered her family fondly, she was overwhelmed with emotion.

In her mind Asabe was telling her family the horrific part when the Boko Haram threw her down and beat her and she cried out, "There is a God! There is a God!" She shook her head and wondered what had caused her to say it.

Then she smiled, her face still buried in her hands. From the depths of her heart there arose a silent cry, *Yes, praise the Lord, there is a God!*

Chapter 8

Ladi

It was Sunday. Or if you speak Hausa, it was *Ladi*.

The whole mountain hushed as a song wafted its gentle tones down over the valley. Even the birds held their peace. All nature seemed to step back, as if allowing the song to fling its worship all the way to the high heavens where the Master of the song received its meaningful praise.

Sitting on the ground in a small dell between the mountain's rugged, rock-strewn peaks, the 150 Nigerians restrained their voices. They all wanted to sing as loudly as they could, as they used to in the EYN chapels in Gwoza. But now, halfway up the Mandara Mountain range, it was different. Here they sang softly. Even so, the soothing tune and the important message drove the comforting words deep into the hearts of the folks from Gava and brought tears to many eyes.

The date was November 2, 2013. According to the watches worn by a few members of the congregation, it was 8 a.m., the starting time for hundreds of EYN worship services all over northeast Nigeria. Even though hundreds of chapels had been burned, and the Christians were scattered, these sincere Nigerians knew it was time to gather for their worship service. They were learning fast how true the message of one of their favorite songs was.

> Prayer is the key,
> Prayer is the key,
> Prayer is the master key.
> Master key.

After half an hour of singing, Yusuf, an EYN pastor from a distant village, stood before the congregation. Tears welling up in his eyes, he announced, "Brethren, we all remember how we used to worship freely in our chapels in the past. Oh, how times have changed. Some of you are from my church and some are not. But this morning it doesn't matter."

The congregation sat in rapt attention.

"Some of us are safe here on the mountain, but many of our people are missing. And we all know where they are. They are in heaven with Jesus . . ."

The congregation nodded. Some were smiling. Some had serious looks on their faces. Some wept unabashedly, the tears streaming down their cheeks.

"But this morning," Yusuf continued, "praise the Lord, we are safe. And it's Sunday, a day to worship God."

In the congregation, a young man named Charles sat with two little children bouncing around on his lap. Occasionally he looked up toward the high crags of the mountain peaks that flanked the glade they worshipped in. Everybody knew there were two men sitting up there somewhere, keeping watch. If any Boko Haram soldiers would for some reason decide to climb the mountain that morning, the vigilantes would see them coming. And if a whistle blasted down the mountain from one of the vigilantes, the worshippers would quickly scamper to their caves.

"Brethren, as we sang today, prayer is the master key . . ."

I wonder how my wife is doing, Charles wondered. *O Lord, help her please!*

Brother Yusuf was one of the few refugees up on the mountain who had a Bible. He opened the book reverently and found the passage where Jesus said His followers need to take up their cross daily. "Brethren, taking up Jesus' cross and following Him is not easy, is it? But we all know it is necessary. And being up here on the mountain these days is all part of taking up our cross. If Jesus was persecuted for our sake two thousand years ago, why shouldn't we be willing to suffer persecution for Him today?"

While Yusuf preached his heart out to the people, sharing comforting words that the Holy Spirit gave him, another scene was taking place not more than five hundred yards away.

In the core of the mountain, in a dirty cave, a hush fell upon a group of women who were not able to be in the church service that morning. They had other business to take care of.

Urgent business.

"How's it coming, Margaret?" an elderly woman in her seventies whispered. "Are the pains steady?"

"Yes, Sarah," Margaret whispered, "they're steady and regular." Her dark face was flushed and beads of sweat glistened on her forehead.

Margaret's mother, Mary, sat beside her daughter, holding her hand loosely. "I think everything will be okay," she encouraged her.

Margaret laid her head back on the thin rug she was lying on. *This is so different from the hospital where I had my other babies,* she sighed. *Having my third baby in a cave, with just my mom and her friends to help me, is sure different! I must be brave. I asked God to help me during this time, and I believe He will.*

Margaret stared at the ceiling as her thoughts journeyed far and near.

Ladi

The candlelight drew comical swirling images on the rocky ceiling of the cave. Several bats squeaked incessantly from an adjacent room. *This hard cave floor sure isn't as comfortable as my bed at home,* Margaret grinned to herself.

Margaret remembered distinctly how, a little over a month earlier, their family had fled Gava. It had been a night of terror, watching the church house and other houses burn as they slowly climbed the mountain, knowing that people were being killed or taken captive. Heavy with child, she had climbed the mountain slowly, clinging to her husband Charles's arm. Though his family and many other folks from town had surrounded them, it was a horrible night. All she could think of as they fled was, *What will happen with my baby now?*

I am glad I told my husband to go to church this morning, Margaret mused. Then she smiled. *He wouldn't be any help in the cave anyway. It's a women's moment!*

"Lord, please help me to have this baby quickly," Margaret prayed earnestly. "You see these conditions I am in, lying here on this cave floor without even a blanket. But you can do a miracle and this baby can be born even here among the bats."

Suddenly the pains got harder.

Today is Sunday—Ladi, Margaret thought, bracing for another wave of pain. *I will call my baby Ladi.*

An hour later one of the ladies gently laid a crying bundle on Margaret's chest. "It's a girl, Margaret," she whispered. "And just as we hoped, everything is all right."

"Praise the Lord!" Margaret exclaimed, clutching the baby to herself. "Praise the Lord! She was born on the Lord's Day, so I will name her Ladi. I love that name because it's the day the Lord rose from the dead."

"Margaret," Mary whispered a while later, "are you strong enough to sit up and eat a little draw soup? I made it especially for you from baobab leaves. I also have some mush that I made from maize."

Though the soup lacked several basic ingredients, it tasted delicious to the recuperating mother and gave her the nourishment and strength she needed.

Little Ladi was a tough baby. Was it because she was born in a cave? Two months later, when Charles and Margaret decided to try to escape, Ladi was ready to travel. Instead of going over the mountain into Cameroon as most of the others did, Charles took his wife and three children and sneaked down into Gava one night. Skirting the towns occupied by Boko Haram, he took to the fields he knew so well. Later they came out on a main highway where Charles caught a ride to Kwarhi. There, the EYN church was providing food and shelter for refugees like them.

Charles's mother and his sister Lydia, also trying to escape with her three children, did not fare so well. They were captured by Boko Haram on the way down the mountain, and Charles had no idea what happened to them or where they were being held.

After they were settled in Kwarhi, Charles and Margaret often talked about how God had delivered them, and thanked Him for His protection. "Here in Kwarhi we have everything we need," Charles reminded his wife often. "Though we can't go back to Gava to work on our farms yet, things are going well for us. Just think of my mom, my sister, and their children . . ."

"And our little Ladi is growing by leaps and bounds," Margaret agreed happily. "Though she was born in an unusual maternity ward, she is healthy and such a joy to our family. I can never thank God enough!"

Ladi

Chapter 9

Pumpum "Orphans"

The bright African sun was doing its job faithfully, as if trying to bake the group of captives, making them sweat as they trekked down the sandy dirt road from the village of Kelle to the city of Lassa. No merciful clouds swept between the sun and the earth to cool off the group of women and children. No breeze floated across the harsh land to give the group some respite. The three soldiers who escorted them, decked out in green, faded fatigues, also found the heat stifling, and their dark faces dripped with sweat.

Abigail Madu, a tall, slender twelve-year-old girl, led Monday, her five-year-old sister, by the hand. And little Jonathan, two years old, rode along grandly on Abigail's waist. After several hours of walking along under the hot sun at the cruel soldiers' pace, Abigail was exhausted, and little Monday was lagging.

Two rebels brought up the rear guard. "Get going!" one of them barked. "We'll never get to Sambisa if you dawdle like this!"

This is so unfair! Abigail thought. She felt like crying. Up ahead, the leader walked along at a leisurely pace, carrying his gun. *You terrorists are used to hiking across these plains,* she complained in her heart. *But I am not. And I am carrying my little brother. I can hardly go anymore.*

"Cooperate or I will kill all of you!" the angry Boko Haram soldier snarled, pointing his AK-47 at them. "I could easily kill you. So get going, and don't complain."

Abigail was troubled. Not only were they captives to the terrible Boko Haram, but it seemed life itself was dealing them a terrible blow. Not only did she have herself to worry about, but she also had the responsibility of caring for her siblings.

An older lady, Madame Hamadama, noticed how tired Abigail was, carrying little Jonathan. She stepped over and offered to take the baby for a while. Abigail didn't say a word as she handed the baby over, but the gratitude in her heart was immense.

The three young children had lived with their parents, Madu and Amina, in a village called Pumpum, close to the city of Lassa. After Boko Haram descended on Pumpum, the family fled to Lassa. Later, when Boko Haram hit Lassa, the family fled to the little village of Kelle.

But once again, they were not safe for long. The morning Boko Haram struck Kelle, Abigail's parents were away looking for a place for the family to live as refugees. They had heard rumors of a Christian refugee camp for people who were running from Boko Haram.

When the gunfire started in Kelle, Abigail and her siblings ran with some neighbors toward a wooded area. The whole town soon discovered that Boko Haram had surrounded the village before they attacked. They caught Abigail and her siblings, along with several other neighbors, as they fled in panic, running for the hills.

The date was December 14, 2014.

After Abigail and her siblings were kidnapped, they were forced to walk to Lassa. Then, after spending the night locked up in a vacant house, the soldiers escorted them and a number of other captives on another long walk to Pumpum. But instead of entering the village that had been Abigail's home, a truck picked them up. Four hours later they were unloaded like cattle in the Sambisa Forest.

The soldiers decided to take them farther into the forest to another camp, so they were soon on the move again. The travel conditions were brutal, with the soldiers constantly goading them to walk faster. Though the soldiers gave the captives food, it often wasn't much, and it was usually eaten on the run. The soldiers seemed merciless and constantly insulted them, calling them infidels, but that did not bother Abigail too much. What broke her heart and overwhelmed her was little Jonathan's distress.

"Mama! Mama! Mama!" he cried every night at bedtime. He could not understand why his mother wouldn't come to him and put him to sleep as she used to. And though Abigail tried again and again to explain their situation, Jonathan did not understand. All she could do was put her arms around him as they both cried themselves to sleep.

Abigail found it was easier to explain the situation to Monday. It was becoming clear what a brave girl the five-year-old was, and though she too asked for her mother each evening, she seemed to take life in stride. After hearing Abigail explain that God would take care of them, she would lie down on her old Arabic rug and go to sleep fairly easily.

It became clear that the three children were slaves, along with the fifteen other captives. And once they got to their destination, they discovered they were only a small part of a large network of slavery. Old men, women of all ages, and many, many children were all part of Al-Barnawi's terrorist camp. And the terrorist leader knew little mercy. Abigail and her siblings soon tasted this truth.

Abigail's group of fifteen joined a group of ten that slept in a house with adobe walls, a tin roof, and a packed dirt floor. The house stood among a number of other houses that accommodated dozens of other captives. It had several bedrooms where the captives slept on thin Arabic rugs. They cooked outside, under a makeshift lean-to.

Madame Hamadama became the undisputed leader of the group. Not only was she efficient and showed authority, but she was spiritually mature. Everyone was glad she took the lead.

Abigail's life became a labyrinth of constant work. It seemed that if there wasn't enough work, there was someone trying to invent more so the captives could be kept busy. Every morning they began at the crack of dawn, just as the Abyssinian rollers, large blue birds with a screeching call, started flashing their aqua glory as they sallied from the treetops to catch insects. They then worked until late at night when the crickets shrilled their incessant goodnight refrain. All Abigail did, it seemed, was work, work, work!

Abigail's job description included anything the soldiers could think of. She cooked, washed dishes, swept the dirt floors, washed clothes, shook or washed the Arabic mats that were used for everything, brought in firewood, started fires, ran errands, took care of children, and did a thousand and one other things.

In a way the hard work was a blessing for Abigail. At night she was so tired she would collapse onto her rug and fall asleep immediately, often with Jonathan in her arms. And she slept soundly until morning. Also, during the day she did not have time to sit around and worry. Although she was responsible to watch out for her siblings, work helped the time go faster.

Little Monday was a blessing. She not only had an easygoing personality, but she even helped Abigail with the work. The biggest thing she did for her older sister was to watch over little Jonathan, and she took her job seriously.

Jonathan was a quiet, introverted boy, and it was not easy for him to adapt to the harsh conditions at Al-Barnawi's camp. He cried a lot and found it hard to warm up to the other children in the camp and play with them. What bothered Abigail the most was the way the Boko Haram soldiers treated the sensitive child. Although they treated all their captives like dogs, they were especially mean to children.

The worst incident came one day when Abigail caught the emir of the village telling little Jonathan why they kidnapped boys. "Someday you will be big," he explained, hunching down in front of the terrified boy. "Then you will learn to be a fighter. You will become strong and learn to handle this toy." He chuckled as he caressed his well-kept rifle. "You will really make this thing bark."

Little Jonathan just froze, sitting on the ground, his eyes big and round. He didn't understand a thing except the tone of the rasping voice. Abigail was mortified and angry when she heard the emir finish his tirade. "You will become a good Muslim," he said with a smirk. "You will enjoy jihad. You will learn to hate and to kill the infidels. And you will go back to Pumpum and shoot your daddy!"

Though Abigail was tall for her age and resembled a skinny child, she was often the brunt of lewd jokes by the Boko Haram fighters she met daily.

"Someday you'll grow up," a soldier sneered one day, winking at her maliciously. "You will get pretty. Then we will place you in a marriage. But for now you are way too skinny!"

For once Abigail thanked the Lord that she was skinny! But she also worried about the time when she would fill out and become a lady. *I need to find a way to escape. But when will that be? They guard us so carefully.*

The group of captives Abigail was with had been asked to renounce Christ as soon as they arrived at the camp. Because she was considered a child, Abigail had not been present. She noticed, however, that most of the ladies soon wore hijabs.

One day the ladies came from a session with the emir and reported how they all had to be washed with a lot of water. "I think the Muslim women in charge were trying to wash Christendom off our bodies, getting us ready to receive Islam," Madame Hamadama muttered in disgust. "It's their way of baptizing us."

Abigail was soon forced to wear a hijab as well. She also had to participate in the Muslim prayers and the study of the Koran, the most dreaded activities for the slaves.

But there were also things that encouraged the captives and kept them going, such as the times when Madame Hamadama helped the group find precious moments to pray. Madame Hamadama always waited for the times when the guards were not around, such as midmorning, midafternoon, or in the evening after the soldiers went to bed. At such times, she would walk around among the captives, winking. Everyone knew what that meant. They would all gather in the main room of their house, the same room they were locked into at night. Then, with someone keeping watch at each door and window, the rest quickly knelt in a circle to pray.

Abigail was never sure which she enjoyed more, the fervent prayer in the circle or the excitement of standing guard. When she stood at a window or a door, she was thrilled to feel Madame Hamadama's courage and hear the low murmurs of the prayers. She prized the feeling of responsibility for something so daring and so right.

The captives learned to be careful in their praying, and during the whole time that Abigail was captive, they never once got caught. They had many close calls, and their Boko Haram superiors suspected the truth, but they were never able to prove anything.

One of the things Abigail learned from Madame Hamadama was to pray in faith. Like Madame, she found herself praying for the Boko Haram soldiers' souls and salvation. At the end, everybody always prayed for an opportunity to escape. *When will God answer our prayer?* Abigail wondered daily. In awe she expected the answer to be soon. *At least before I am forced into marriage,* she prayed earnestly.

Whenever any of the captives didn't obey orders, or let it slip that they were still loyal to God, the soldiers would threaten them with a horrifying prospect. "If you don't obey, we'll take you to Al-Barnawi!" they would say. It was a threat that Abigail and her fellow captives, fortunately, never had to taste.

Because it never happened, Abigail never knew why that was such a terrible thing. They could only imagine. Al-Barnawi lived in another village close by. Fortunately, Abigail never saw the man, but she heard enough to realize what an ominous, terrible leader he was.

To Al-Barnawi, killing someone in cold blood was as easy and as common as taking a few peanuts and pitching them into your mouth. The way he treated the slaves was also reflected in how his soldiers treated the slaves. *The emir was trying to teach Jonathan to hate his daddy, then later kill him. What would Al-Barnawi teach him?* wondered Abigail.

One day God Almighty decided that the captives had suffered enough. Most of Al-Barnawi's army left one afternoon to raid a town called Damboa. The next morning they came back devastated. Damboa had been well prepared for a Boko Haram raid, and the Nigerian army had ambushed Boko Haram with all their forces during the raid.

Abigail was shocked when their trucks drove into the plaza of the village and started unloading bodies out of the back of their truck. "Just see how many were killed!" Madame Hamadama whispered. "It looks as if most of them were killed! Poor boys!"[1]

Madame Hamadama saw how devastated the soldiers were. A tired, defeated air hung over the few men who returned alive. All of a sudden she started winking at the others, and as usual they met in the main room of their house, but this time it was not to pray. Madame Hamadama put a few women at their lookout stations, then she looked at the rest with those authoritative eyes and hissed, "Tonight we escape!"

---

[1] They later heard rumors that 90 percent of the soldiers who went on that raid were killed.

Everybody in the group nodded, their eyes big. "Prepare food and water, whatever you can carry. We leave at 10 p.m. Everyone be awake and ready."

As if in a dream, Abigail spent the day working as usual. Whenever she had snatches of time, she prepared a little sack of things she and her siblings would need for the journey, including the few items of clothing they had. *No hijab!* she thought gleefully.

Abigail found a bottle and filled it with water. Then she started filling a small bag with some groundnuts, ground maize to make porridge, some bread the men had brought back from the raid, and a handful of dates. *If Boko Haram can survive on dates, so can we,* she chuckled to herself.

In the late afternoon Abigail got Monday and Jonathan to take naps. They didn't want to and couldn't understand the urgency in Abigail's demands. They didn't know what their night would be like, and Abigail could only imagine.

As the hour approached, so did the tension among the group of captives. At first the soldiers had always locked the captives in, but when no one tried to escape, they became careless. That night the front door was padlocked, but the back door was left open.

At 8 p.m., soon after dark, Madame Hamadama went out and gathered what they needed to cross the wall, which stood head high around the courtyard. It was too high to vault, so the ladies quickly stacked concrete blocks in the back corner. "That should do," Madame hissed, and motioned for everyone to return to their quarters and wait.

At 9:30, Madame Hamadama sent a lady to check if the soldiers' quarters were quiet. Minutes later she was back, whispering, "Everything is quiet. Apparently the soldiers are all asleep. Nobody seems to be on guard. Let's go!"

They all slipped out into the courtyard. Fortunately, there was moonlight, so they didn't need to use flashlights. Not using flashlights would help them escape undetected. The whole thing had to be done quickly and quietly.

Madame Hamadama was the oldest, so they helped her cross the wall first. She had agreed to go first and help find the way after everyone had crossed. But once she disappeared over the wall, everything got a bit crazy.

No one wanted to be the last to cross because they were afraid they might get caught. They were also worried that if they delayed, they would get left behind. The crossing of the wall became a miniature stampede, with everyone pushing to get over next, the older helping the younger.

Abigail stood back and let everybody else cross. Then, as the last girl jumped up onto the wall, she hissed to her, "Help me get the children across!"

What Abigail didn't know was that Madame Hamadama had gone on ahead, and so the girl who had just crossed was too scared to help. Suddenly Abigail found herself all alone. And since leaving her siblings behind was not an option, she got busy doing what she had to do.

With her heart screaming for the others to wait, she threw her sack over the wall. Then, carrying Jonathan, she crawled up onto the block barricade. She plopped him up on the wall, whispering comforting words to him so he wouldn't cry, then scrambled up onto the wall herself. The boy clung to her tightly.

Meanwhile, Monday had climbed up onto the pile of blocks and was reaching her hands up desperately. Somehow Abigail, who was on top of the wall holding Jonathan with one hand, leaned over and took Monday's little hand and hauled her up.

This was a precarious moment, with Abigail trying to keep her balance while hanging on to the two children. "Look, Monday," she gasped, "you have to hold on by yourself, so I can jump down."

Monday lay down on the wall and clung like a monkey. Then Abigail helped Jonathan do the same. *He's so brave,* she rejoiced. *He still hasn't cried once.*

Swiftly Abigail jumped down off the wall, then told Monday to let herself slide down to her. She caught her and helped her to her feet. She had to coax Jonathan for several minutes until he was willing to turn himself loose from the security of the wall. Finally he slid down into Abigail's arms, crying softly.

Abigail grabbed her sack and threw it over her shoulder. Then she heaved her little brother up onto her waist. Last of all, she grabbed her sister's hand, and they fled into the night. From the moment she had seen that the other fugitives had abandoned them, terror had gripped her, and now she sobbed aloud. In vain she tried to quell her panicky thoughts. *If the soldiers catch me, they will kill all three of us!* Desperately she tore through the bushes until she found the road.

Abigail had a general idea in which direction the others had gone. She got on her hands and knees in the middle of the road, checking for tracks in the dust in the dim moonlight. She recognized the shoe prints of the others, then headed up the road as fast as she could. All the while, she refused to look back, afraid that some Boko Haram terrorist would be following.

Madame Hamadama's plan was to take the road until they got some distance from the village. Then she planned to leave the road where their tracks were not easily visible and cut across the fields. The hope was to get to distant villages that were not allied with Boko Haram. It would be a lot harder for the soldiers to track them in the wooded areas where the grasses hid their tracks.

"Lord, please help me find the rest!" Abigail panted as she walked along as fast as she could with the big load she carried. "Lord, show me the way."

Feeling a clear leading to stay on the road, Abigail decided to put as many miles between her and the awful memories of Al-Barnawi's camp as she could. After a mile, she heard a low shout from a cluster of trees just off the road and recognized Madame Hamadama's voice. Relieved to the core, she turned in their direction and ran to join her companions.

Madame Hamadama had decided to wait on Abigail in a cluster of trees beside the road where they planned to detour into the bush. She now gave Abigail a quick hug and apologized for panicking and letting them sit. "All's well that ends well," she added, shaking her head in obvious relief. "I was so worried for you and your little ones. Did you see any signs of anyone following us?"

"No," Abigail panted. "Everything was quiet when we left."

"Let's go!" Madame commanded briskly, turning toward the bush. "With all those bodies to bury, I don't think the soldiers will worry about us, but you never know. The best thing for us is to get out of here as fast as we can!"

The food and water lasted for two days. After that they begged for food from the Fulani villages they came through and drank from the cow ponds like the Fulani herdsmen did. The Fulani were usually kind and gave the fugitives something to eat, even if they themselves were poor. They were also afraid of Boko Haram and felt a kinship with the fugitives.

One morning before the sun was blazing, Abigail saw another Fulani village up ahead. She was shocked again at seeing how small and poor their little shacks were. *They could pack up their makeshift tents and be ready to travel within the hour,* Abigail mused. *But that's because they are Bedouins. They are a traveling people and carry everything they own on their backs and on their donkeys' backs. They follow the grass for their cattle and sheep. That's all that matters for them.*

As they got closer to the village, Abigail was fascinated by a large herd of red cattle that milled around to one side of the little tents. The adult cattle all had huge sets of white horns that stuck up into the sky. Whenever they moved or shook their heads, the horns would flash in the sunlight. Even little Monday and Jonathan were interested in watching the free show.

Apparently a rich Fulani man owned a lot of cattle, and now he and his sons were out milking them. Speaking in Hausa, Madame Hamadama told the owner what was happening. He hollered into the shack in the Fulani dialect, and a child ran out with several gourd bowls. Then, dipping out of the buckets brimming with milk, the kind man gave each of the children a bowlful.

That night the group of captives again slept out under the stars on their rugs. But for once Abigail's heart was happy. As she looked up into the dark sky, watching the stars twinkle down upon them, she smiled. Then she prayed, "Dear God, thank you because tonight little Monday and Jonathan have their tummies tight full of milk."

For five torturous days, Abigail carried one and sometimes two little children under the blazing sun. The travelers finally arrived at a little village where Madame Hamadama approached the first house and told the people their story. The people of the house were understanding and promised to give them food and water.

Abigail plopped down under an immense neem tree, the two little ones still clinging to her. *I feel more tired and thirsty than I ever have before,* she sighed. *And hungrier. I think I am nearly starved. And the children are probably even hungrier than I am.*

While their hosts prepared the food, Abigail downed glass after glass of good clean water, sharing with her siblings. Then she leaned her head against the neem tree's trunk and closed her eyes. The Sambisa Forest now seemed far away. They were finally free. They had been captives of Boko Haram for a month and three weeks. Now, after five days of walking, the ordeal was finally over.

Abigail was excited because she could see the road that would lead them to Pumpum. But would her parents be back home again in Pumpum? She didn't know. Her heart seemed to pump extra fast. She opened her eyes a slit and saw that little Monday had fallen asleep leaning against her. Jonathan's eyes were closed as well.

Then the next thing Abigail knew, they were waking her up because the food was ready.

"Poor girl!" the woman of the house exclaimed when she saw how exhausted Abigail was. "Poor little children! How can mankind be so mean as to make these precious children suffer like this? But come on in. I have some rice and beans ready for you to eat."

The next couple of days were both happy and sad. The kind people from the village helped Abigail and her siblings travel to Lassa, and then on to Pumpum. Unfortunately, once they got home, the three young children discovered that their family hadn't come back home yet. After making arrangements to stay with their grandmother, they discovered that Boko Haram was still harassing the village. Several times they had scary experiences while staying at their grandmother's place.

Meanwhile, Abigail's mother, Amina, heard that her children were in Pumpum. Too afraid to go there herself, Amina sent a man on a motorcycle to pick them up, but the children refused to ride back with him. Not because they were afraid of crowding onto the cycle—that was totally normal in Nigeria—but because they didn't know or trust the bearded man. Little Jonathan was especially afraid, and he ran to his sister crying in panic. Abigail understood. The man looked rough—and way too much like that Boko Haram emir!

The next day Abigail's mother decided to take the bus to Pumpum herself to pick up her children. When the three children saw her coming, they all burst out crying and ran to meet her. Abigail ran so fast that she knocked her mother over as they embraced. Quickly they picked themselves up, and Amina, still on her knees, took in the two little ones. As they embraced, they pushed their heads together and wept. Abigail stood sobbing as she watched the sacred scene. Monday and Jonathan had a mother again. Finally. And she too suddenly realized how much she needed her mother.

After the great reunion, mother and children rode the bus back to

Yola where Amina was staying. Their father, Madu, who had a job in another city, soon came to meet them and was overjoyed at seeing his missing children again. He decided it would be safer for everyone to go along to the city where he was working. "We will live there until things stabilize in Pumpum," he told them.

One evening, a week after they had been reunited as a family, they were gathered in the living room after the evening meal. Upon impulse, Madu asked little Jonathan what he remembered most about their time with Boko Haram. Jonathan didn't say a word, but Abigail could see he was thinking. A sad look washed over his face and his eyes got bigger.

Please, Dad, be careful or you will frighten your sensitive little son, Abigail thought, wincing. Aloud she said, "Jonathan, I am so glad you don't remember what Boko Haram tried to teach you. Fortunately, you were too little. You will never remember their wicked plans for you."

"And what were those plans?" Madu asked innocently.

Tears welled up in Abigail's eyes as she told her father what the emir had told Jonathan. "That's the kind of terrible doctrine they teach. Think of it. The emir told him he should someday go home and kill his daddy!"

Madu shook his head sadly. "Yes, they teach a terrible terrorist doctrine. But there is Someone who is more powerful in northeast Nigeria than they are . . ."

"That's right!" Amina cheered. "Jesus is much greater, and He is the one who brought you children back home safely! You will never know, children, how much I worried for you."

"And prayed for you!" Madu threw in. "Your mother was constantly praying and fasting for your safe return."

"And He answered our prayers," Amina replied. "Praise the Lord!"

Abigail discovered that tears were running down her cheeks again. "You are right, Mom! So right. That was the longest and most dangerous two months in our lives. But somehow I knew all along that God would see us through."

Twilight settled over the house gently, and as the fireflies blinked their tiny lights in agreement, the three Pumpum "orphans" enjoyed the blessing of not feeling like orphans anymore. The whole family was together again, in a safe place, surrounded by love and peace.

"Let's not forget to pray for the Boko Haram terrorists," Abigail reminded the family as she leaned against her mother, enjoying her warmth and love. Then, glancing at her father, she added, "And I'm so thankful, Daddy, that you are alive, and we feel safe because you will take care of us."

Though the living room was silent now, everyone's heart was singing. Abigail was especially grateful. "Thank you, God!" she whispered. "Thank you a thousand times over for traveling to Sambisa Forest and back with us, keeping us safe. Amen!"

Chapter 10

An Ant-Infested Prayer Chamber

*I*t seemed as if northeastern Nigeria had gone into silent mode. A hush had fallen over the lazy river and its arid surroundings. No breeze rustled the leaves on the nearby trees. No birds sang among the branches as the hot noon hours ticked along. Only some ants were moving, and it seemed they were exploring something big that had crashed into their dry old ditch down beside the river.

The something had hair and it wore a dress, but no shoes. The ants soon discovered that the lady lying in the ditch had some bare skin. So they bit. And it hurt!

Hajaratu Yohanna, a single sister from the EYN church in Michika, was lying in the ditch, every so often sneaking her hand down to squash the ants that were biting her legs. Otherwise she tried to play dead. It was becoming harder and harder to pretend she wasn't there, especially since she was feeling sick and the ants were eating her up.

Hajaratu lived in a tiny apartment on the spacious compound of the EYN John Guli Bible College on the outskirts of the town of Michika, Nigeria. She was in her early thirties and taught school on the campus. That morning, Hajaratu had awakened with a fever and a headache. *I must be getting the flu,* she decided. *I hope I don't get worse. This is Sunday and I'd like to go to church.*

Because Hajaratu loved the Lord and enjoyed the worship services so much, she decided to take a pain pill and get ready for church. When it was time for the service to start, Hajaratu felt better. She walked to the chapel, which was also on the compound and only a stone's throw from her apartment.

The church service that Sunday morning had been inspiring, as if God knew what was coming and blessed the congregation with fervor and joy. The believers had worshipped together, singing and praising as if it were their last opportunity on earth to do so.

For some it was.

After the service had ended, Hajaratu went to her apartment right away. *I need to lie down and rest a while till I feel better. Maybe if I take a nap . . .*

Suddenly Hajaratu's world was shattered when she heard distant gunshots. She jumped out of bed and stepped out into the courtyard that lay between her apartment and the pastor's house. The pastor and his wife burst out of the house at the same time. Soon they were running from house to house and to the dorms of the compound, warning people to run down to the river and then on to the bush.

Meanwhile, the Boko Haram soldiers were doing their usual looting, burning, and killing in the surrounding town. Because they hate western education, they were making their way steadily toward the college.

Not until everyone was warned and running did the pastor and his wife escape, heading across the fields for the bush. They were followed by Hajaratu and a few others. Although it had taken only a few minutes to warn everybody, by the time they left, the soldiers were already beginning to invade their compound. Since Hajaratu wasn't feeling well and was not a good runner, she was soon lagging behind the others. She started to panic. *I'll never make it! The soldiers will catch me long before I get to the bush!* In desperation she flung herself into a dry ditch and flattened out. Trying to calm her frantic heart, she prayed, "O Lord, please watch over me! You know what those wicked men might do to me if they find me here in this ditch. O Lord, have mercy on me . . . Please blind their eyes."

Hajaratu never found out how close the bandits came to her hideout, as she never lifted her head to see. In the distance she heard loud noises, and then she smelled smoke. The Lord blessed her by not letting her realize that her own apartment was burning to the ground, or that the chapel was being totally destroyed.

If it hadn't been for the ants, Hajaratu might actually have slept through the ordeal. As it was, she was feeling so sick that she dozed off in a groggy stupor. As the hours ticked by, the ants became worse and worse. By three in the afternoon, Hajaratu couldn't take it anymore. It was as if they had decided to eat her alive, and now dozens of the critters were chewing on her. Realizing she could not possibly squash them all, she lifted her head in desperation to see if anyone was around.

Suddenly a man came walking along the ditch right where she lay. Terrified, her eyes sought his face. *Is he friend or foe?*

It was one of the village leaders. He and his helpers were walking around assessing the damage. Immensely relieved, Hajaratu tried to get up. Her body was cramped and stiff. The men were shocked when they saw a lady crawling out of the ditch, but as soon as they recognized her, they helped her up. She shared her story, and then the men decided it was time to move on. They all headed toward a neighboring village, but because they were afraid that town had also been attacked by Boko Haram, they hid in a maize field until it got dark. Then they found an

An Ant-Infested Prayer Chamber

empty house on the outskirts of town and spent the night there.

The next morning, Hajaratu caught public transportation to Lassa where she had relatives, and from there she went on to safer cities. Not until four months later was she able to come back to the John Guli Bible College compound in Michika.

One morning after returning home, Hajaratu stood outside and stared at the sky. Feeling safe and much better physically, she started making a mental list of everything she was thankful for.

When I was in the ditch, I was sure I was going to die. Not only was I sick, but the ants were eating me up. And if the Boko Haram soldiers had found me huddled there in the ditch, they might have molested me, or even shot me. Praise the Lord that He kept me safe!

Hajaratu smiled to herself. She realized that in spite of the ants, God had provided a safe place for her. For three long hours, He had blinded the soldiers as they did their dirty work close to where she lay. Right under their eyes, God had provided a little refuge just for her.

Chapter 11

The Old Reverend and His Gown

Old Reverend Matthew sat and stared at his two friends. The three men were enjoying a moment of fellowship as they waited for the noon meal. The EYN church service, held in the chapel in the compound of the EYN John Guli Bible College, had just ended and they had met at the principal's house to wait on the noon meal. Matthew had just thrown his pastoral gown onto the principal's desk and was in shirt sleeves waiting for the principal's wife to serve her delicious food.

Boom! Boom! Boom!

Was that gunshots? Old Matthew listened intently, frozen to his seat. *That was close, right outside the courtyard wall!*

The next thing he heard was the wild Muslim cry, *"Allahu Akbar! Allahu Akbar!"*

"It's Boko Haram! Let's run!" the principal of the college hissed.

Like all the other Christians, their hearts were filled with terror when they heard that phrase, and it didn't take the group long to obey the principal's urging. Since the gunshots had come from the street out front, the fugitives ran for the back of the courtyard. Quickly they scampered over the low courtyard wall.

About that time two Boko Haram rebels found the front courtyard gate and rushed inside, expecting to ambush their prey. Old Matthew was the last person to clamber over the low courtyard wall, and a Boko Haram soldier saw him just as he disappeared over the top.

Providentially, a field of tall maize was right behind the courtyard. One second after Old Matthew crashed into it, zigzagging like a scared rabbit, the soldiers opened fire. But since they didn't know where to aim, the bullets flew into the maize randomly and harmlessly.

The refugees gathered at the outer edge of the maize field, relatively safe. Suddenly a frantic look came over Matthew's face. "I left my pastor's gown in your living room!" he wailed.

Before anyone could convince him how dangerous it was to return to the house, Old Matthew was running back through the maize, slipping through the rows like a deer, determined to retrieve his gown.

Once Matthew arrived at the courtyard wall, he peered over it to see if the way was clear. What he didn't know was that the two Boko Haram soldiers had slipped over the wall and were tiptoeing through the maize, trying to find them. Had God blinded their eyes so they didn't see Matthew returning?

Seeing that everything was quiet, Matthew jumped over the wall and ran into the house, unaware that one of the soldiers had gotten a glimpse of him as he dropped over the wall. Just as Matthew was grabbing his gown, the soldiers were approaching the wall to scale back over to get him.

After retrieving the gown, Matthew returned to the back door to head out across the maize field again. Suddenly he saw the first Boko Haram soldier come up over the wall, flailing his rifle. Turning around, he quickly dashed out the front door. But instead of running out onto the street to his sure death, he veered to the right where the principal's garden lay. And again, providentially, this was planted in a thick stand of sugarcane, which provides even better cover than maize.

This time the bullets ripped up sugarcane instead of maize stalks. Old Matthew zigzagged just as he had before. At the back edge he held still for a bit, then popped out of the sugarcane and tumbled over the wall—unscathed. The soldiers gave up. They had easier victims to seek.

Minutes later Matthew met up with his fellow Christians as they evacuated the maize field and made their way toward the wooded area beyond. The group had been worried, praying fervently that the soldiers wouldn't shoot their friend.

When Matthew marched into the clearing, he triumphantly held up his gown. "I got it!" he cheered. "I did not want those wicked men to use my gown to deceive innocent people before killing them!"

"You're right," the principal agreed, nodding vigorously. "Those wicked men could have worn that gown to dress up as a reverend and then enter a church with a suicide bomb."

After hearing the story of Matthew's adventures, they hiked back into the wooded area. While they trekked toward a neighboring village, the principal added another thought. "God loves you a lot, Matthew! I declare, being shot at twice by Boko Haram soldiers and coming out unscathed both times is nothing short of a miracle."

Matthew nodded, wiping sweat from his brow. "God protected me because He knew that retrieving that gown was important." He held the gown to his breast. "God knew I had to get it back. And I knew it too. He made it all work out. And here we are, safe and sound. Praise the Lord!"

Chapter 12

Mercy and Peace

The poverty-stricken neighborhood at the outskirts of Uba was in chaos that sad evening. It seemed people were running everywhere but getting nowhere. Some were screaming, while others were yelling out warnings—"Boko Haram! Boko Haram! Boko Haram!"

Everybody was desperate, trying to get away from the gunfire that roared from two directions. Panic-stricken, people tried to determine which way to flee, even as the gunfire was getting closer and closer. The noise sounded like a battle in a major war.

Among the masses, Godia Paul anxiously tried to make sense of the situation. Unfortunately, she couldn't see and could hardly hear. But her oldest daughter, Mary, who was eight years old, was tugging at her hand and yelling into her ear, "Mother, we need to run! It's Boko Haram!"

"Where is Peace?" Godia yelled. "Make sure the children are all with us!"

Mary lifted two-year-old Peace and shoved her into her mother's arms.

When Godia had been a twelve-year-old schoolgirl, she had contracted polio. The dreadful disease had attacked both her eyesight and her hearing. Ever since then, Godia's world had been dark—and very quiet.

When cute Godia was merely fourteen years old, her parents had married her off to a man named Paul Alimi. His dowry was simple because of Godia's handicap. But four children later, Godia knew they had a good marriage in spite of her blindness.

Now, as Mary clutched her mom's hand and led her as they ran down the road toward a village called Uvu, they realized that the terrible thing everyone had feared was finally happening. The Boko Haram terrorists were attacking their city.

Running along beside Godia, clutching at her skirt, was six-year-old Ezekiel. With her left hand, Mary pulled along little four-year-old Emmanuel, who bumbled along trying to make sense of what was happening.

All Godia could do for her children now was hold tightly to Little Peace and run as fast as she could. She prayed that the rest of her children were all running along beside her. While they ran, Godia's mind raced almost as fast as her feet. *What will happen to us now? With Paul in the city, we will have to fend for ourselves. And me being blind and nearly deaf. Oh thank you, Lord, for my Mary! She has become my eyes and my ears!* As the fugitives panted down the road, Godia squeezed Mary's hand, the hand that continually clung to hers and guided her.

Godia worried for Little Peace, and she squished her baby to her breast even as she hurried along. *I guess God will have to take good care of a baby that's so small,* she sobbed to herself, slowing her stride as they limped into Uvu. *I sure hope God will take care of my husband. Without Paul, I don't know how I could raise our four children!*

There was one advantage in being blind and practically deaf that awful day in November of 2014. As Godia escaped with her children, she never saw the sky turn red as Boko Haram's flames burned up church houses, as well as other houses and businesses owned by Christians. Nor could she hear the screams of her dying neighbors.

After four days, Paul finally located his wife and children. He joined them in Uvu, and they decided to stay there for the time being. But after running out of food, Paul got ready to make a quick trip to their house in Uba to bring food.

"But isn't it dangerous, Paul?" Godia worried, when she heard his plans.

"Yes, it is," Paul answered. "But staying here is not a solution either. If we don't have food, we will starve. The children are already hungry."

Godia knew her husband was right. They decided to enjoy the evening together, then that night he would set out. She smiled as she realized Paul was taking time to play with the children as a way of saying goodbye. Last of all he held Little Peace for a long time until she went to sleep in his arms.

After the children were sleeping, Paul and Godia had a heart-to-heart talk. "I don't know why your trip to Uba worries me so," Godia admitted, running her fingers through his kinky hair. "Couldn't we find another solution? Can you imagine what life would be like for me with my handicap if you were killed?"

Paul understood. "But I just don't see any other solution," he replied, looking at his wife tenderly. "I will be careful. Surely Boko Haram has left Uba by now and it is safe."

Godia reluctantly saw Paul off during the wee hours of the next morning.

The long wait for Paul's return was torturous. As the day crept along and they heard nothing, Godia's heart sank slowly. *What could be taking him so long?*

That night Godia slept little, knowing something was terribly wrong.

The next morning an army truck drove up in front of their rented house. Two grim-faced soldiers met Godia and Mary at the door. "We have bad news," one of them said hesitantly, as they looked down at their feet. They felt sorry for the lady who stood there staring into space, obviously blind. "Boko Haram terrorists shot and killed your husband. We have brought the body so you can bury him."

Godia didn't show any reaction.

But that's because she didn't hear a word they said. Nor did she see. Not until Mary pulled her mother's head down to her level and shouted the sad news right into her ear did she understand. Then Godia and Mary both started crying.

Bloody and bullet-riddled, Paul's body was placed on a crude table. As Godia leaned over the body, her tears flooded down onto his lifeless face. She was seeing her husband as only the blind can. Her deft fingers, laced with the wetness of her tears, traced Paul's facial features over and over.

"Paul, I was afraid this would happen!" she cried, dropping her forehead down onto her husband's. "Oh, how I need you! Oh, how I will miss you! Paul, why did you go?"

The three oldest children—Mary, Ezekiel, and Emmanuel—clung to their mother's skirt as she cried over her husband's body. Suddenly Godia remembered her children. Hunching down to their level, she put her arms around them and wept with them. "Children, at least we have each other," she assured them bravely. "And we have God. He will help us, even if Daddy is gone. And because I have you, I will be able to go on with life. We will work together."

Life did go on. Both sets of parents and the EYN church community helped Godia with the funeral and the burial. Godia moved in with her parents in Kwarhi. Later an organization called Christian Aid Ministries from the United States built her a house on land that belonged to Paul's family. Godia learned to live one day at a time.

Anyone would think that Godia had suffered enough, but her cup of affliction was not drained yet. There was another dreg she needed to swallow.

One morning Godia got the family up at the break of dawn. It was a cold morning, and the children looked for something to wrap around themselves to provide warmth. Little Peace, now five years old, found a thick rug that would serve as her mantle.

"Let's pray before starting the day," Godia announced, like always. They all knelt in a circle in the living room and Godia led in a sincere prayer. As usual, Godia didn't close her eyes. She didn't need to.

Next she stepped out into the courtyard, her children following. With Mary's help, she started the fire on the hearth in the courtyard. Mary carefully placed a pot of beans on a triangle of rocks placed around the coals to cook their breakfast. The children huddled around the blaze, seeking warmth that was slow in coming. Wrapped in her rug, Little Peace sat on a rock close to the fire and warmed her bare toes.

Godia did what she had loved doing her whole life, even after she was blind—she got to work. Taking the short-handled broom, she swept the courtyard clean. During the night, leaves had fallen from the trees. She swept these leaves together and burned them in the fire while the beans cooked.

The whole eastern horizon was turning a peach color. The large trees surrounding the courtyard looked like giants, raising their branches like long arms as if to embrace the light of the new day. The trees were indeed a handsome band of silhouettes against the blushing sky. But Godia couldn't see the beauty or hear the birds that were just starting to trill in the treetops.

Suddenly the tranquil morning was rent by a scream from the direction of the fire. Godia's heart lurched to her throat when Mary yelled into her ear, telling her what had happened. This was the kind of crisis Godia had always feared. She knew that Little Peace was in trouble, but she could do nothing except grope her way over to the cooking site and scream for help.

"Help! Help! My baby is burning!" Godia's hoarse cry joined in with

Little Peace's shrill screams. "Mary, get help!"

Fortunately, a neighbor lady named Mercy was walking past the courtyard gate when the screaming started. Mercy quickly sized up what had happened. The rug Little Peace was sitting on had gotten too close to the fire and had started burning.

Mercy raced to the scene and tried to take off the screaming little girl's burning dress. But the knot at the belt was too tight, and all Mercy got for trying to help was a set of burned hands. Meanwhile, Little Peace's skirt burned upward and ignited the top part of the dress. Just when Mercy was giving up in despair, Mary came running with a bucket of water. Grabbing the bucket, Mercy poured the water over the little girl, and the flames died down immediately.

Mercy helped Mary flag a tiptop[1] while Godia held Little Peace, who was writhing in terrible pain. Quickly they rushed her to the hospital.

Godia did not allow her handicap to keep her from staying at her little daughter's side the next few months as Little Peace fought for her life. They spent one month in the Uba hospital, then two weeks in the Mubi hospital. Things weren't going well, so they decided to transfer her to a larger hospital in Yola. Despite all their efforts, Little Peace's burns were too severe, and one day Jesus took her home to be with Him in heaven.

A week after Little Peace had left her earthly home, Mercy came to visit Godia, wondering how she was faring. Once again, Mary hollered whatever Mercy said into her mother's ear, and the broken-hearted mother cried as she talked about the ordeal. "What was so hard was to be there during Little Peace's crisis but not being able to do anything to help," Godia said. "I couldn't see and I couldn't hear. I just couldn't tell what was happening. I felt so helpless . . ."

Tears welled up in Mercy's eyes as she heard her neighbor's frustration. How could she encourage this distraught lady? What Godia said

---

[1] A motorcycle taxi.

next blessed her.

"But I don't want to complain," Godia announced, getting control of her emotions.

Mercy nodded, watching Godia's face intently.

Godia continued, her blind eyes brimming with tears. "Several years ago, Boko Haram hit our neighborhood in Uba. It's a wonder they didn't catch me and my children and kill us. As you can imagine, I was such easy prey. That's how I know God loves us and has protected us all the time."

"It must have been hard when they killed your husband," Mercy told her with feeling.

Godia nodded. "Yes, that was one of the hardest things for me. Since I am handicapped, it would seem that I needed my husband more than most women. But then again, God knows what's best. And guess what I thought of this morning in my prayers."

"I can't imagine," Mercy replied, wiping the tears from her eyes.

"In a way I am glad God took Paul home when He did," Godia sobbed. "Because that way Paul was there to receive Little Peace when she got to paradise. Can you imagine the joy for them both as Paul welcomed her home, then held her on his lap upon her arrival?"

Mercy was overwhelmed and didn't know what to say. Godia ended the conversation by saying, "Thanks so much, Mercy, for doing what you did for Little Peace!"

Chapter 13

Rejoicing Anyway

The hospital walls were snow white and the room smelled like alcohol. A young lady in her early thirties lay on the hospital bed, as still as a corpse. Though the nurses could barely see her chest rise and fall, she was still breathing. Wadiam opened her large, coal-black eyes groggily. *I am in the hospital,* she moaned, throwing her head to one side. *They have operated on me twice and I am not getting any better. I need to accept it. I am going to die.*

The hours dragged by slowly for Wadiam as she felt herself growing weaker and weaker. Her mind, however, was awake and she remembered so many things. *I have had a good life. I have always loved my large family. My brothers and my sisters. My father and my mother. Yes, despite all the difficulties and the stress of growing up in a poor area like northeastern Nigeria, life has been good!*

Wadiam lovingly thought of her husband Sabon. They had been happily wedded on December 27, 2013, and now, three months later, she was going to die. Her husband had been so good to her. Wadiam wondered where he was now. *I am sure he will stop by later today after his hospital calls.*

Saratu, Wadiam's mother, stayed with her daughter during this difficult time in the hospital, but she had left this morning to meet with another of her children, Jasini, who was a registered nurse. She wanted him to help with Wadiam's care.

"Oh God!" Wadiam prayed earnestly. "Be with me as I travel through this dark valley of death. I can feel my life's strength draining out slowly. In your Word you promise to go with me. That's why I rejoice. Even my name, Wadiam, means to rejoice! Because you are here with me, I can rejoice. If it's my time to go, take me home. I am yours!"

Wadiam, who had grown up with her family in Uba, had moved to Maiduguri when she married Sabon, a psychiatrist. He had taken a job in a hospital in another part of the city.

One morning after Sabon had left for work, Wadiam had suddenly experienced pain in her abdomen. The pain was almost unbearable and Wadiam was writhing in agony. Finally her mother, who was in Maiduguri visiting her daughter, helped her hail a taxi to go to the hospital.

The doctors found Wadiam to be pregnant, and thought she also had an ulcer, which they treated for three days. But nothing helped. Wadiam was still wasting away, not being able to eat, so they scheduled her for surgery the next day.

For the next two days, however, Maiduguri was in an uproar because of Boko Haram attacks in several parts of the city. The doctors were afraid to even come to the hospital. Wadiam and her mother faced two long days alone, with Wadiam suffering immensely. By the time the doctors finally ushered her off to surgery, everyone knew things were not well.

The surgery revealed that Wadiam did not have an ulcer after all, but an obstruction in her intestines. By now, her intestines were black and gangrenous. The doctors did what they could, removing two thirds of her intestines. The operation seemed successful and they put her on a special diet, including an expensive nutritious milk. Everyone prayed that she would recuperate.

During this time her mother faithfully stayed by her bedside and Sabon stopped by when he could, but the city was often locked down. Other family members also visited her when they could. But each passing day made it plain that Wadiam was not getting better.

When it was finally decided that Wadiam needed another operation, they scheduled it for the next day. But the next day Boko Haram hit the city again, and the whole town went into an emergency mode. The doctors hunkered down in their homes and couldn't get to the hospital.

Two days later the doctors were finally able to operate on Wadiam, but what they found confirmed the truth. It was too late. They cleaned Wadiam up the best they could but left the wound open so it could drain.

Once the family discovered that Wadiam was low, her brother Jasini said he would try to come and help.

Wadiam realized that her time was near. She lay on her bed, motionless, thinking about her death. *Oh, I wish Sabon would be here. But I doubt if he can make it.*

Suddenly the silence in the hospital room was broken as Saratu and Jasini entered the room. Jasini rushed to Wadiam's bedside, then knelt down and clutched her pale hand in both of his, tears streaming down his cheeks. Saratu knelt at the other side of the bed and began telling him the tragedy of the last several weeks.

"Oh, Jasini, if it weren't for Boko Haram, she might have had a chance," Saratu wailed, wringing her hands. "But every time there was an emergency, the doctors were not on call. And now she is in really bad shape."

"Mother," Jasini began, "she is in God's hands . . ."

"Listen," Wadiam interrupted, holding up her weak hand, "I am not too young to die. I am in God's hands, and that is a good place to be. May His will be done. Everything is okay."

Mother and brother were silent. It astounded them to think that Wadiam had accepted her death before they had. They were struggling to cope with their own feelings.

"I just wanted to tell you not to worry about me. I am prepared to die. Please serve God faithfully so we can be together again in heaven."

Saratu and Jasini were weeping, but Wadiam's eyes were dry. She had no tears for her own grief, though she was worried for the family. "Please tell all the family what I said. Don't give up on God! And He won't give up on you."

As an afterthought, she added, "And thanks so much, both of you, for taking care of me!"

"Well," Jasini announced, jumping up suddenly and turning to leave the room. "Here we sit talking. I have to go for help. Surely I can find a doctor somewhere who can help!"

"Come, Jasini," Wadiam demanded in a weak but clear voice. "Kneel down here again and take my hand. Mother, you too. It's too late. It's okay. I am almost gone."

It was a sacred scene. The dying lady lay still on the hospital bed. Her sobbing mother and brother knelt, one on either side of the hospital bed, grasping the two cold hands as if their life depended on it.

"Tell Sabon I love him and I say goodbye," Wadiam whispered. "I wanted so much to give him a baby. But God had other plans."

Suddenly Wadiam's eyes opened wide as she stared at the ceiling. A smile formed on her pale face and there was a flush of great joy. Then, in a whisper so low that her two companions had to lean close to hear and understand, she gasped, "Let's run! They are coming to pick me up. Let's go . . ."

Was it the angels?

Then Wadiam was gone. She had left this old world according to her name—rejoicing!

Chapter 14

Saratu's Turkey Gobbler

The bright African sun smiled down upon a spacious courtyard bustling with activities. Birds sang in the bushes and trees that thrived along the edges of the courtyard. The Sunday morning sun kissed the flowers that bejeweled the bushes and made the packed courtyard's dirt floor glisten.

Toward one end of the courtyard, under a porch off the tiny kitchen, a young damsel named Asiburyu smiled as she pounded guinea corn into flour in a wooden mortar. Her smile was almost as bright as the morning sun. And she knew how to work!

Asiburyu was fourteen years old and had recently been adopted by the Ishaya family. She and her younger sister Jummai had been orphaned years ago. The Ishaya family had adopted Jummai when she was small, while Asiburyu had gone to stay with her late father's relatives. Later, the Ishaya family took Asiburyu as well because she was having problems in her adoptive home.

Eight-year-old Jummai was sweeping the courtyard's earthen floor with a short-handled broom. Because of the difficult life they had lived so far, both sisters were used to hard labor. Now, in the Ishaya home, things were so much better for them. They not only worked hard to show their appreciation, but they were happy.

Joshua, the Ishaya family's 24-year-old son, was sitting under the porch of the house that perched on the opposite side of the courtyard. He was also smiling, happy because he had just filled his stomach with his mom's porridge. His mother had a way of making him content by feeding him what he liked.

Joshua was studying at Kulp Bible College in Kwarhi, not far from their hometown of Uba, so he often came home for the weekend. As usual, he was looking forward to attending the EYN church with the family that Sunday morning. He was also looking forward to a noon-day meal with the family, especially since his mother had announced that she was preparing turkey soup for lunch.

Family life was good for Joshua at this stage of his life. The home activities that he missed so much at the boarding school were such a pleasure on the weekends.

"I am so glad Kwarhi isn't far from home," Joshua sighed, smiling at Asiburyu. "That way I can come home most weekends and enjoy your and Mom's wonderful cooking."

Asiburyu smiled back at her adoptive brother. Of all the family, she liked Joshua best. He was always kind. And so understanding. And when he was home, he kept the family laughing with his constant jokes. *Joshua will get somewhere in life,* she thought, smiling at him as he laid his bowl aside and leaned back in his chair. *He is so smart and dedicated to whatever he decides to do.*

Everybody looked up when their mother, the manager of not only the courtyard but the whole household, stepped out of the house. Her colorful African dress seemed to flow along with her body's movements as she stepped out onto the bare patio. Saratu Ishaya was a respected and efficient housewife, and she was always on the move.

Saratu had been up since the crack of dawn, supervising the cooking and cleaning, as well as feeding her family. Now it was time to feed her many animals. Every morning the creatures waited hungrily just across the low adobe wall where the courtyard continued into what looked like a small zoo.

Every morning Saratu filled a bucket with guinea corn out of the large sack on top of the firewood stacked on the kitchen porch. Then, bucket placed upon her hip, she opened the gate that led to a larger section where the animals stayed at night. Along the courtyard wall stood several little adobe domes that resembled ovens. At the base of each dome was an opening closed by a little door. Saratu went over to each dome and opened the little doors, releasing a batch of chickens that dashed out, hungrily accosting their benefactor for breakfast.

Saratu then addressed the flock of chickens of all ages and stages that came running to her feet. "Whoa, there!" she yelled, shooing them away with her free hand. "Take it easy. There is enough guinea corn for all of you!"

After filling the various wooden troughs perched at the edge of the courtyard, Saratu turned to take care of her pride and joy—a pair of handsome turkeys and their offspring. Saratu smiled as the tom lifted his head and gobbled long and loud. After she had filled the small wooden box that served the turkeys, she watched them eat, ready to yell at any bold rooster that dashed over to steal their food.

After the turkeys were satisfied, Saratu opened the gate out onto the dirt street. Since their home was at the edge of town, all the animals were allowed to slip out of the courtyard and wander down to the end of the short street. There they went into a wooded area for the day. In the evening they all came back home, ready to find their domes to sleep in till the next morning.

After taking care of the fowl, Saratu opened a wooden gate to another courtyard that had higher walls. As she opened it, she yelled, "Get back, Billy!" knowing she would be ambushed by the goats. The big billy goat, with a long, flowing beard, was lowering his head as if to ram into his owner. But Saratu laughed heartily. "I know you, Billy. You wouldn't hurt a flea!"

Saratu filled the goats' trough with guinea corn and slammed the gate shut again. Within an hour, she would return and let the young goats out to mingle with the chickens in the outback. But the older stock she kept inside, knowing they could do a lot of damage to neighboring gardens if they were free for the day.

Ishaya Bzugu, Saratu's husband, was a construction manager who built houses, having several men working under him. Right now he was working in Port Harcourt, a city hundreds of miles away in southern Nigeria.

On this fine Sunday morning, Joshua stood in the bustle of the courtyard and smiled as he thought about his family. He had nine brothers and sisters, and though most of them had already married and left home, he loved them all. Now he was home for the weekend and his two adopted sisters were busy, one sweeping the courtyard and the other grinding guinea corn in the mortar.

Joshua's parents had put thought into picking names for their children. "Names are important and should have meaning," Ishaya always declared. "And if we are Christians, they should carry spiritual meanings."

Joshua grinned as he thought about his own name's meaning. *My Savior . . . That is a good name. Jesus is my Savior, and now that I follow Him, I can help to save others.*

Joshua grimaced as he remembered the sad story of his sister Wadiam. *Wadiam* meant "rejoice." They had named her that, and she had lived up to it. Yes, she had rejoiced till the end.

Joshua thought of Barka, his next younger sister. Her name meant "blessing." And she was such a blessing to all of them! Next in line was his brother Jafiya, whose name meant, "God keeps." Then Kmar, which means "patience." *We are such a happy family,* Joshua rejoiced. *God has been so good to us!*

But that was before Boko Haram came to visit Uba. Though the whole family realized that someday their happiness could be taken away, they still weren't prepared for what happened the very next week.

When the soldiers arrived, Saratu, like a mother hen, took her children still at home and ran for their farmland outside the village. There she hid with them in the middle of a large field of maize.

Saratu sometimes sneaked back to her house to feed the animals she had left penned up. She would then take back things they needed. Sometimes she would get some grain or perhaps catch a chicken to take along back. Their house was at the edge of the city and close to the woods. Going home was easier for her than for most of the fugitives, who were hiding farther away on the Mandara Mountain range. And that's why, in spite of the crisis, Saratu's courtyard survived.

One day Saratu was surprised to see that her husband had come back from Port Harcourt and had managed to find them in the maize field. "I came to take you with me to Port," he announced.

Saratu was surprised at Ishaya's proposal. *In a way I want to get out of here,* she mused seriously. *But in another way I feel responsible for our animals and our homestead.*

Ishaya waited patiently, watching his wife's expression. But he couldn't tell what she was thinking.

"There are rumors flying all around that things are not going well for Boko Haram," Saratu replied pensively. "Many people think they will soon abandon Uba and head back to where they came from. If I knew that were true, I'd want to stay. I feel so torn."

"It's up to you," Ishaya said. "If you decide to go with me, we leave early in the morning. Jafiya is also going along. But if you want to stay, that's all right."

Saratu's Turkey Gobbler

Saratu decided to stay.

Often Saratu made the daily trip to her house after dark. But one day she needed a chicken to make a special Sunday meal, so she decided to sneak to the house in the daytime. At the edge of a nearby field she watched their street for a long time for any signs of movement.

Finally, convinced all was well, she crossed the gully that lay between the field and her street. Looking up the street, she was again satisfied that the way was clear. She sprinted up to their gate, knowing it was much safer in the courtyard than on the street.

Once Saratu arrived at the gate, she still couldn't see into the courtyard. The walls along the street were high and the gate was covered with upright sheets of tin. Quickly she opened the gate and stepped into the courtyard.

When she was safely inside, she closed the gate and tiptoed across the chickens' courtyard. She was just ready to slip through an open gate into the smaller courtyard that lay between the kitchen and the house when she stopped suddenly. Shocked beyond measure, she froze—and stared.

Three men were sitting in a circle, sitting on low stools, busily eating. Before she could react, all three Boko Haram soldiers looked up and returned Saratu's stare.

It's too late to run, Saratu realized, her heart dropping to her knees. *I am totally at their mercy. What will they do to me?*

Seeing Saratu, one of the soldiers jumped to his feet, grappling with his AK-47 and almost knocking his chair over in the process. "What are you doing here?" he barked.

Almost too shocked to speak, Saratu finally squeaked out a reply. "I came to feed my chickens."

The terrorist had pulled up his gun as he talked, but Saratu noticed he didn't look angry enough to shoot. It seemed he actually saw some humor in the situation and was almost at the point of cracking a smile. Then, to her shock, he did.

"You had better be glad you found us happily eating this delicious soup we made with your turkey gobbler. That makes us content," he grinned, patting his belly with his free hand. "We are too happy and satisfied to kill anybody right now, so why don't you just get out of here? And don't come back if you know what's good for you!"

Saratu obeyed. Quickly. She turned on her heels and fled.

The encounter left Saratu shaking with fear. "We should have gone with Father," she told her daughters. "It is not safe here."

The next day Saratu and her daughters took public transport to Port Harcourt. Ishaya was surprised, but welcomed her with a big smile. "I'm glad you're here," he told her. "I was concerned about you."

A few weeks later, however, when they received word that the soldiers had left Uba, Saratu didn't hesitate. "I need to return home," she said. "I have to see if my animals are still alive."

A few days later, she was back in her happy courtyard, starting over with her remaining chickens and goats. She was so happy that the soldiers had left a few stragglers from her chicken flock. But most of all she was glad that the terrorists had retreated back north, taking their atrocities with them. Hopefully they would stay away for good.

With Saratu and her two children back home again, things finally looked more promising. It was a day of rejoicing when Ishaya was able to join them. Joshua also soon returned to Kwarhi to continue his studies, so he was able to come home at times.

To Saratu's disappointment, only one lonely turkey hen remained in her courtyard. The Boko Haram soldiers had not only eaten the gobbler but all the young stock. Saratu knew she would want to somehow find a mate for the hen so she could again raise turkeys.

In the whole ordeal, one fact stood out—Saratu's special turkey gobbler had most likely saved her life. Because of its tasty death, the soldiers had allowed her to escape. As she once again diligently took care of her household, Saratu often paused to thank the Lord for His love and mercy.

Saratu's Turkey Gobbler

Chapter 15

A Deep, Deep Sleep

Not again! Joshua Ishaya moaned, shaking his head as he watched the Kwarhi people running past the Kulp Bible College campus where he was studying. He turned to his two friends who were standing beside him at the school entrance. "Can't these people learn that it's just another false alarm?"

Samson, also a student, nodded in agreement. "This is not the first time they think it's a Boko Haram attack when it's just the army showing off their gun power."

"There have been at least ten false alarms!" Joshua complained bitterly. "Once I fled town and spent a week in Jos. Another time I fled and ended up in Kano. But it was always a false alarm! Think of it, traveling over 300 miles for no reason at all."

"But someday it might actually happen," Joshua's friend Mathew spoke up. "We should be ready at all times. Kwarhi might not go untouched forever."

"You're right," Joshua replied. "I remember well when they hit my hometown of Uba, and that's not so far away. But I'm not going anywhere until I really have to. I'm tired of running from nobody."

Samson agreed. So the three young men stayed put that fateful morning even as almost everyone else headed for the bush.

At midmorning people were still running by sporadically. The sprawling campus of Kulp Bible College was nestled between the town and the big wide bush beyond. When the townspeople wanted to escape, they automatically headed for the bush, and that's why a lot of them raced right through the campus.

Meanwhile the boys continued hearing distant gunshots. What finally made Joshua wary was the fact that they seemed to be coming closer. He also noticed that the people who fled past them had eyes wide with fear. Yet he was determined to prove that this was just another false alarm.

Time ticked on.

Suddenly, without warning, their peace was shattered by a loud explosion. A bomb had hit, very close. In panic, the three boys jumped to their feet. It didn't matter anymore if it was a false alarm or not—it was time to get out of here! The three ran desperately after the other townspeople.

Fortunately, there was a stand of head-high maize right behind the campus. The three young men plowed into it and crashed their way to the center of the field as if their life depended on it.

Pausing in the center of the maize field, glad to be alive, Joshua and his friends needed to make a serious decision. *Where do we go from here?*

"Let's head east and cross the mountain to Cameroon," Mathew suggested, wiping the sweat from his forehead. "This is bad! If the Boko Haram soldiers catch us they will force us to deny Christ or die, and I don't want to do either!"

"I don't want to go to a refugee camp either!" Joshua answered, shaking his head vigorously. "Anything is better than that." He was thinking of all the horror stories he had heard about the camps.

Samson took Joshua's side, suggesting, "Anything but Cameroon! My hometown is Makera, and if we manage to get across the main highway, we will be within walking distance of my village."

All three boys knew that the only option other than heading east toward Cameroon was heading west toward the main highway. Unfortunately, that area was probably held right now by Boko Haram. "We will have to risk crossing the highway," Joshua decided, taking the lead. "We will wait till after dark and slip across and head to Makera, then on to Hong."

They found a huge baobab tree that extended its wide branches in every direction. It provided shelter from the hot sun as well as a little security since the area was overgrown with brush. They felt much less exposed once they flopped down by the tree's massive trunk to rest.

As they lay silently under the gigantic tree, Joshua's thoughts started to whirl. *What if we meet up with Boko Haram today? What if they find us lying here under this tree? What would my reaction be? Would I be willing to die before renouncing my faith? Would I be able to testify to those wicked men even though they might kill me?*

These and countless other questions raced through the three young men's minds as they lay low over the hot noon hour, thinking, swatting gnats, and wiping the sweat from their faces.

Suddenly Samson jumped up, announcing, "I am going to go look for food. I am starving!"

Joshua and Mathew joined him, heading toward the highway that they feared, looking for food. The maize was still too young to have ears, but they found a bean field that had young, tender beans dangling thickly on the vines. Forgetting all manners, and never even wondering if raw beans were edible, the three boys fell to. Though it tasted funny to ingest such a vegan fare, their hunger was appeased a little.

They finally came to a river that ran brown between its red clay banks. Having no other options, they knelt by its banks and drank their fill of what looked, but didn't taste, like chocolate milk. They then crossed the river and continued their slow trek to the east.

Toward evening the three fugitives heard vehicles roaring past on the highway in the distance. Edging closer, hiding in a thick cluster of trees on a knoll, they could see the highway. "A convoy of Boko Haram trucks is on its way to Kwarhi," Joshua speculated, in a whisper. "We have to be careful!"

After the trucks roared by, Joshua led the group closer to the road, moving stealthily from bush to bush and tree to tree. "The road seems empty now," he hissed. "Let's make a run for it."

"Are you sure?" Mathew whispered. "If they catch us we are dead men, unless we renounce Christ and join their ranks."

"It looks clear to me," Samson agreed with Joshua. "Let's give it a try."

Seconds later the three ducked through the fence that skirted the road. Once they were on the road, Joshua's fear left him. There was no one around. *But wait a minute. Whose red pickup is pulled over to the side of the road? That looks like my friend Zachariah's pickup.*

Joshua stopped in the middle of the road. "What's wrong?" Samson yelled, concern written all over his face. "Why do you stop?"

"I think that's Zachariah's pickup. He might be having trouble," Joshua answered, still looking up the road.

"Let's run!" Samson insisted, turning to follow Mathew, who was sprinting across a shallow ditch on the opposite side of the road. "This is terribly dangerous!"

Joshua followed, but slowly. He could hardly force himself to leave a friend who might be in need. After crossing the ditch, Joshua met with his two friends under a tree. "I am going back," he announced. "There is no one around, and I can't leave without knowing if my friend is all right."

Joshua returned and crossed the ditch again, keeping his eyes on the red pickup. He was ready to cross the road when he saw what looked like a mere youth step out from behind a tree just beyond the pickup. He was dressed in full army regalia and was brandishing an AK-47.

Quickly Joshua dashed back across the ditch and rushed for the field beyond. By the time he crashed into the tall stand of sorghum, the bullets were following him. Running and zigzagging like a rabbit, Joshua ran faster than he had ever run before. He could hear the bullets ripping up the stalks around him, but not one hit him.

The three friends regrouped beyond the sorghum field and hid behind a baobab tree, panting. "My, that was close!" Samson exclaimed.

"That's for sure!" Joshua echoed. "I wanted to help Zachariah, but they were guarding the place in case somebody decided to do just that. It was a setup that almost cost my life!"

"I wonder what happened to Zachariah," Mathew threw in. "I wonder if they killed him."[1]

The distraught boys walked on into the evening, heading toward the little village of Makera where Samson had relatives. Finally, worn out and famished, they stopped and slept under the trees in the bush.

The next morning they broke their fast on some groundnuts they had dug up from someone's field—and some more raw beans. They also found some fruit they were able to pick on the way. "At least we won't starve," Joshua joked as they walked along. "But we sure won't be gaining any weight either."

They were getting close to Makera when they noticed a family tagging along behind them, headed in the same direction. The boys were glad to see the group of several ladies, a few men, and some children. "At least we can see they aren't Boko Haram militias," Samson chuckled, glancing back from time to time.

"They are probably from Kwarhi, same as us, and running for their lives," Joshua agreed, also on his guard. "They seem in a hurry, because they are catching up with us."

Up ahead, Joshua noticed a huge baobab tree beside the trail. Its

---

[1] The soldiers had shot Zachariah earlier that afternoon, and his dead body was in the pickup when they passed by that fateful evening.

gnarled buttresses propped up tightly to the foot of the tree and boosted the massive trunk upright into the sky.

As the boys approached the massive tree, they heard a pitiful cry coming from the tree. "It sounds like a baby crying!" exclaimed Joshua, who was taking the lead.

When they got closer, they discovered the mystery of the pitiful cry. Apparently a mother who was fleeing for her life had decided to stop under the tree to rest. She had hunched down among the buttresses, laid her back against the tree's trunk, and fallen fast asleep. Now her newborn baby was crying desperately, probably because it was hungry.

"I think the mother is sleeping," Joshua whispered as the boys passed by. The motionless mother was dressed in typical, colorful Nigerian garb. Her headpiece was wrapped neatly around her hair in the style of most ladies from Nigeria. Her eyes were closed. The half-naked baby was squirming desperately, flailing its tiny hands and feet in her mother's lap.

"That baby is probably starving," Samson concluded, moving on past and making a sad face.

"Why doesn't she feed it?" Mathew wondered, shaking his head. "Poor child!"

Joshua's heart felt a deep sadness for the poor baby. *Will it survive? Why doesn't that careless mother wake up and take care of her baby instead of letting it starve?*

The young men had slowed down because of the mother and the child under the baobab tree, so the family behind them had nearly caught up. The boys saw that the family also noticed the lady and the crying baby, so they stopped to see what the family would do.

"She must be sleeping," one of the women announced, stepping over to the pair. The baby was crying harder than ever. The lady spoke to the mother as she reached down and touched the sleeping lady's cheek. Suddenly she jumped back as if she had touched a snake.

"She's dead!" the lady cried, covering her face with her hands.

Immediately Joshua's heart flip-flopped. "The poor woman!" he cried. "I can't believe this!"

They wanted to run over to see what they could do to help, but they also knew they needed to get to Makera soon. And Joshua wanted to head on to Hong that day yet. Leaving the baby's fate to the other group, they pressed on.

Looking back from a distance, Joshua saw that the lady who had discovered the dead woman was tenderly taking the baby into her arms. *That lady will take the baby and find a home for it,* he sighed, a warm feeling settling into his heart. *That's the way mothers are!* Joshua knew that if she couldn't raise the baby herself, she would give it to the government, and they would place it into one of the many orphanages springing up all over because of the Boko Haram persecution. At least now the baby should find a home quickly.

As the boys hiked the last mile to Makera, a prayer sprang up in Joshua's heart. *God, please help us during this terrible time of suffering at the hands of Boko Haram! What are we coming to? To think that a mother must die on the trail, leaving her newborn baby crying in her cold arms! Will anyone even bury the mother, or will she lie there under the tree to be eaten by wild animals?*

"O God, please take care of that tiny baby!" Joshua groaned, his heart breaking and tears welling up in his eyes. Then, almost as an afterthought, he choked, "And take care of us as well!"

Chapter 16

The Garkida Surprise

Like a dark cloud, an enormous hush hung over the town of Garkida on the evening of August 17, 2013. But the people of the town were oblivious of any danger, their eyes glued to their TVs. Ambrose Emmanuel was only one of the many folks watching an international football match between Nigeria and Spain. A large percentage of the Garkida folks could think of nothing except the outcome of the game.

Suddenly Ambrose heard shouts of children running down the street past his house. It took a while for his brain to stop concentrating on who was winning the game and to understand what the desperate children were yelling. "They are coming! They are coming!" they shouted.

Jumping up from his sofa, Ambrose strode over to the door that opened out to the street. "Who is coming?" he yelled into the evening dusk.

"Boko Haram!" the children answered as they rushed by.

Then Ambrose heard what he should have been hearing all along—the sound of gunshots in the distance. *Boom! Boom! Boom!*

Ambrose immediately did what everybody else in Garkida did. He promptly forgot the game and ran for his life. While he and many others ran, desperately seeking a hiding place from terror, a menacing caravan entered town.

Four vehicles charged up to the checkpoint just outside town, shooting as they pounced. Six Nigerian soldiers were killed and one escaped. The caravan then moved on up to the entrance of the town and slowly drove down Main Street. The back of each open vehicle was crowded with a rowdy mob of men and boys dressed in army fatigues. Raising their AK-47s, they shouted, *"Allahu Akbar! Allahu Akbar! Allahu Akbar!"*

Boko Haram had come to Garkida.

As the caravan drove through town, Charlie, a mentally handicapped man, got riled up by all the hollering and the frenzy of the stampeding people. But he didn't run. Innocently, he decided instead to defend the town. Grabbing a stick, he ran to stop the caravan. A Boko Haram militiaman gunned him down on the spot.

Ambrose and several of his friends crashed into a large cluster of grass under a tamarind tree in the bush behind their house. While the caravan drove up and down the Garkida streets, shooting and yelling, other Boko Haram soldiers looted stores and tried to find the people who were hiding. Ambrose and his friends acted like dead men, burrowing into the grass as deeply as they could. Making matters even worse, a storm that had been threatening all evening finally arrived, and the rain fell in torrents. In a matter of minutes, the fugitives were drenched.

Once, during the long night, Ambrose heard several men approaching the tamarind tree. They circled the tree as if sensing someone hiding nearby. But God used the black of the night and the storm to blind the soldiers' eyes. Finally, unable to find anyone, the frustrated terrorists shot several volleys into the treetop just in case some scared victim was hiding up there.

Ambrose felt leaves fall onto his back as the bullets ripped through the tree. The leaves and the rain continued to fall. Ambrose prayed that God would deliver them from this evil.

After midnight, the Boko Haram soldiers parked their vehicles in the center of town and had a party. They were exuberant that they hadn't faced more resistance. Now that the town was subdued, it was time to celebrate. They brought out bottles of Coca Cola they had looted from the stores.

It was 2 a.m. when the caravan finally moved on again, heading back the way they had come. Before they left, they went to the hospital where the Nigerian army soldiers had their living quarters. Earlier they had shot the four tires out of the Nigerian army's Toyota Hilux pickup. Now they towed the limping vehicle out to the bridge at the edge of town and lit it up. That was Boko Haram's defiant way of saying goodbye to the town and its inhabitants who were still in hiding.

In the wee hours of the morning the people slowly came back to their homes, appreciative that the terrorists hadn't taken the town for keeps. The Nigerians are a tough lot and take life and its hardships in stride. Ambrose, as well as the rest, thanked the Lord for His protection, and life went on.

But big questions were left hanging over the Christians in Garkida. *Why didn't Boko Haram burn our churches, our houses, and our stores? Why didn't they kill more people? Why were we delivered in a way that no other towns in the area were?*

On November 14, 2014, a little over a year later, Boko Haram did a repeat attack on Garkida. This time many more army soldiers were in town, and people were not watching a football match. And this time they had a warning.

Because of the warning, the government sent in extra troops to protect the town. However, when the government saw the havoc that Boko Haram had wrought in a neighboring village the day before, they ordered the soldiers to withdraw. The captain of the army called the local EYN pastor. "We expect Boko Haram to hit in the morning. We are withdrawing. Be ready to run!"

Ambrose was again one of the fugitives, this time running with most of the townspeople for the mountain that towered over them to the east.

Dauda Tarfa, a well-known nurse who worked in the local hospital, decided to leave town at the crack of dawn before Boko Haram hit. Loading his family into his Hilux pickup, he headed out of town, but the timing was unfortunate. The Hilux met the convoy of terrorists head-on.

The soldiers shot and killed Dauda, then dumped his widow and children off beside his dead body as if they were trash. Turning Dauda's Hilux around, they loaded it with bandits. The leader perched on the back, toting a huge flag with Arabic writing on it and an AK-47. Dauda's Hilux led the ominous caravan back into Garkida.

When they got to the center of town, they tried to get all the Muslims together, most of which had fled with the Christians. Lately, Boko Haram was terrorizing the Muslims as well as the Christians, but some Muslim youth did join Boko Haram that night.

When they had rounded up as many people as they could, the leader preached an Islamic sermon to them. "We are here to do what Allah has told us to do. We are trying our best to reestablish the Muslim religion and uphold Sharia law. Join us for a revival of all that Allah has to offer!"

After the sermon, the Boko Haram leaders pulled out drinks and food, and the party began.

This time, the terrorists did more damage than the first time. They ransacked the church houses and schools, and smashed all the musical instruments. They also burned the Bibles and ripped up any other books they found, leaving the scraps strewn around the area. They demolished anything connected with Christian worship and western education, but it was still minor compared to many neighboring towns.

Ambrose and his comrades spent a week up on the mountain in hiding.

At night, they sneaked back to their houses in town to look for food and clothes. They soon saw that it was too dangerous a game. So, like the people in Gwoza, they began harvesting any crops they could find.

While the Christians hid on the mountain, the Boko Haram soldiers lived it up in Garkida and even fed their new Muslim converts with food from the stores they had looted the first night. Though it seemed unfair to Ambrose and his companions, they were just glad to be alive. Especially when they realized how much damage Boko Haram had done in other areas and how many people they had killed.

For a whole week the Boko Haram terrorists held Garkida captive. Then, after the week was up, they suddenly left. It seemed they were having a lot of problems on other fronts. Slowly the Garkida Christians trickled back home and tried to go on with life. What else was there to do?

One evening as the sun painted an orange background on the western horizon, Ambrose was sitting on his mat out in the yard beside Rebeca, his fiancée. As they discussed the recent happenings, Ambrose shook his head in wonder. "I still don't understand, Rebeca, why Boko Haram didn't do more damage here in Garkida. They had a whole week to destroy our town, and especially our churches. But we were spared."

Rebeca admired her husband-to-be. He had recently been promoted to be the administrator of the Garkida school where more than a hundred children were given their education. Ambrose took his job seriously and was loved by all. Now he was deep in thought as he again voiced his feelings.

"I don't doubt that it was God who delivered us from the awful cruelties of Boko Haram. But it's still a mystery what He used to stay their terrible hand both times they hit our town. It seems God did something to cause them to have mercy. Not one building was burned, and very few people were killed. It is just so hard to believe. Throughout all of northeastern Nigeria, Boko Haram has burned down over a thousand churches in the last two years. Hundreds of Christians have been killed and thousands have been displaced. Though it hasn't been easy, here we are, recovering from their attacks."

Rebeca smiled fondly, looking at Ambrose, knowing that he loved to think deeply and to figure things out. "You are right," she agreed. "It is a real mystery. But let's rejoice in God's blessing on our town and wait to see if someday God will reveal to us the mysterious *why.*"

Chapter 17

Mr. Quickly

The wide-open field shimmered like a bronze lake in the blazing Garkida sun. The scene on the field during that noon hour resembled an anthill. But instead of ants scurrying about in their labor, forty African workers were sprinkled over the land, sweating as they dug and poured the footers for the new school complex—all by hand.

The year was 1972.

Under the shade of an immense baobab tree, a forty-year-old white man stood watching the workers, sweat drops slipping down his face. Picking up a water jug, he threw back his head and nearly drained it as his Adam's apple bobbed up and down. Pulling out a large handkerchief from his overalls, he wiped his bearded face.

After a short rest, the man glanced at his sixteen-year-old son and grinned. Then, as if remembering all the work that needed to be done, he sighed, "Back to work, Carl!"

"Daddy," Carl asked, detaining his father, "when is it time for the Muslims to pray?"

Carl had spent most of his recent years at a Christian boarding school called Hillcrest, located over a hundred miles away in Yola. Now he was happy for the school vacation so he could be involved in the building projects with his father.

Pulling out his pocket watch, Owen Shankster answered, "They pray in about ten minutes, son. Sharply at 1:00. It's like clockwork. It never fails. You just watch."

Mr. Quickly, a nickname given to Owen by his Nigerian brothers, strode out onto the field, fumbling for his tape measure that was always hooked on his belt. He didn't let the grass grow beneath his feet, and he expected the Nigerians to work quickly and efficiently too. Carl followed his father to the field.

Mr. Quickly motioned to his helper, Gabriel, a young teenager, and they continued measuring out the last ditches for the footers of the new construction.

Sure enough, ten minutes later there was a stir among the workers as half of them abandoned their work and scurried over to the baobab tree. Earlier that morning, they had left their belongings on a pile among the stately tree's buttresses. Now these twenty men promptly found their water pitchers and mats, then spread the mats out in rows in the shade.

Young Carl found it interesting to watch as the men quickly washed their hands and feet with little squirts of water from their pitchers. Then they all knelt east, toward Mecca, bowing their heads to the ground in prayer. Carl was too far away to hear them, but he had often heard it before. Not that he understood them; they prayed in Arabic.

After the twenty-minute prayer session, the Muslims fished out their lunches and ate their noon meal. The men who hadn't joined the prayers under the baobab tree also found shade under other trees along the field's edge. They rested, eating their lunch and drinking lots of water.

It took a lot of water to keep forty hardworking men hydrated. After a half hour everything returned to normal and the field again looked like an enormous anthill.

That evening Owen, his wife Celia, and the five Shankster children gathered around the supper table. Celia, or Marmbwa[1] as their Bura neighbors called her, had prepared a big meal of rice and served it with homemade bread and lemonade.

"I am really happy with my work crew," Owen commented, looking at Carl with a pleased smile. "The Muslims always take off their twenty or thirty minutes to pray, and at first it was hard for the Christians to accept that I allow this. But now they just grin and bear it."

"Dad," Carl interrupted, wiping his mouth with the back of his hand, "have you noticed that dark spot on Gabriel's forehead? He says it comes from praying so much and from pressing his head against the ground."

"Yes, I have heard of that many times," Owen answered, helping himself to more rice. "But what's sad is that they are proud of how often and how intensely they pray. There is a lot of competition in their praying."

Twenty-one-year-old Don nodded, chuckling. "You know, they even do foolish things to make their spot darker. My friend told me that Gabriel rubs soot on his spot to make it dark."

"That's true," Owen grimaced, pushing back his chair from the table. "They think that by showing off their prayer life they will be better Muslims. But Jesus taught us to pray in private so we don't get human recognition."

"I can just see Gabriel rubbing coal on his forehead," twelve-year-old Janice remarked, laughing at the mental picture. "It's a wonder he can wash the soot off later."

"Let's not laugh at them," Owen admonished his family seriously. "We Christians often misunderstand prayer too. Many Muslims are sincere

---

[1] "Woman of the house."

Mr. Quickly

and just don't know better. It is our duty to help them understand what is right and wrong not only by our words, but also by our example. And everyone deserves respect. Children, let's pray for Gabriel."

The children all nodded.

"I am trying my best to help the Nigerians accept each other," Owen continued, reaching for his Bible to read a daily portion of Scripture to the family. "It has been almost impossible to get the Muslims and the Christians to be at peace with each other. Sometimes I almost give up trying. But today as I watched them work shoulder to shoulder, laughing and visiting, I began to believe that at least here in Garkida it might work after all."

Two gas lanterns hung from the ceiling like grand chandeliers, hissing as they gave off their gift of light. Several black beetles zoomed around the dining room, occasionally hitting the lanterns and dropping to the floor as if dead. But they weren't hurt, just stunned, and soon took flight again. Fascinated by the light, they laboriously continued their circling.

The atmosphere was warm and cozy. In the Shankster residence, there was peace and happiness. But in the distance the family heard the beat of the drums. Carl shivered. The drums always made him feel uneasy. Though he feared no danger in the quiet town of Garkida, the wild music always made him uncomfortable and stirred his spirit in the wrong way.

"This evening we will read from the book of Isaiah, chapter 9," Owen announced, opening his well-worn Bible. "We'll see what God has for us tonight."

After reading the whole chapter, Owen highlighted the phrase "Prince of Peace." Sighing deeply, he stated, "Jesus is our peace. The very Prince of Peace. Why does peace seem so slow in coming? Oh, when will Nigeria find peace?"

"When they find Jesus!" his wife Marmbwa answered, smiling in the dim light. "Praise the Lord that many are finding Him. Think of how many churches have been started since the work began in this area years ago."

"You are right, dear," Owen sighed, staring ahead at nothing in particular. "In heaven we will have perfect peace. What we are striving for here, and what we experience, is a prelude to that wonderful, eternal gift. Meanwhile, we continue to be the peacemakers that Jesus called us to be."

The frogs that croaked from a distant rain pool seemed to belch out a hearty amen.

Marmbwa stared at the big bowl of rice perched on a stump in the middle of the courtyard. She looked at the seven blobs resting on top of the rice and wished they weren't there. *Or if I were only sleeping. Then I could wake up knowing it was only a dream.*

But no, Marmbwa didn't have to pinch herself to know that she was wide awake and what she was seeing was real. Just as she had feared, her American culture was clashing head-on with the Bura culture. *What can I do?* she cried inwardly.

Mr. Quickly knew what to do. "Let's all close our eyes and pray," he announced.

Carl was having a hard time keeping a straight face. *I can't believe it,* he thought. *Dad is even thanking God for the cooked mice!*

The courtyard was full of weather-beaten men and work-hardened women. Half-dressed—or undressed—children surrounded the family, who sat on stumps or on crates set up for the meal. They all wanted to make the Shankster family feel welcome. That's why the Christian pastor of the EYN church and the Muslim emir of the village had collaborated to fix such a grand meal for them. Though the villagers didn't know much about how Christians prayed, they followed the family's example, bowing their heads and closing their eyes.

After a brief prayer in the Bura language, Mr. Quickly did what his staring hosts expected. He daintily picked up a little soaked mouse and brought it to his mouth. Then, aware of what the culture dictated, he bit off its head. As he chewed it slowly, little teeth and all, he smiled at his hosts. Swallowing the bite and smacking his lips, he confessed, "That sure enough is the best part!"

The toughest thing for Marmbwa to accept was that her husband meant it. *Why can't I just enjoy it too?* she groaned inwardly. *What can I do? Just the sight of those hairy, slicked-down creatures almost makes me gag.*

Fortunately, the rest of the Shankster family had also learned some tricks of the trade. Knowing full well how their mother was feeling, the family cooperated. They fell to, making extra commotion, crowding around as they made those mice disappear quickly. Along with the mice, heaping handfuls of rice traveled down the same gastronomic pathway.

Marmbwa did help herself to a handful of rice and enjoyed it, relieved that she didn't have to eat a mouse that day. A warm feeling flooded over her as she watched her family eat with their hands like the Buras. She knew they were true missionaries; they loved the people and the culture. That made her glad. The nagging sadness she had felt at first for not being Bura enough to eat mice soon left her. At least her family understood why it was so hard for her. She just hoped the hosts hadn't noticed that she hadn't eaten any of the specialties of the day.

Several villagers had come to the Shanksters' home in Garkida and had asked for a well for their distant village. Owen had made the conditions clear. "Okay, sirs, you go home and call a meeting, and I will come to your village on Saturday to explain how we dig wells."

That Saturday, after a meal, Mr. Quickly was ready for the meeting.

"Are all the village men and boys here?" Mr. Quickly asked as several dozen men and boys surrounded him. "If not, this well project is all off."

The villagers nodded vigorously.

"Are you all willing to jump in and help dig this well?"

Some of the men looked a little uneasy. The emir was not nodding this time.

"Either you help dig," Mr. Quickly announced, "or if you think you are too good to dig, you have to pay someone to dig for you at a wage that I decide. If you won't all do your part in digging this well, I go home. That is our policy."

The men agreed.

"Okay," Mr. Quickly explained, "today is Saturday. I will be here on Monday morning, and we will start digging your well. Lord willing, in a week you should have all the healthy, clean water you need."

In total, Owen Shankster and his family lived and labored in northeast Nigeria for forty years. Arriving in the 1950s from Indiana, Owen knew Stover Kulp well and worked under his direction for a number of years. He too enjoyed the thick shade of the tamarind tree and often wondered how old the town's patriarchal plant really was.

Like the Stover Kulp family, the Shanksters had their share of joys and sorrows. Missionary life in Africa was tough but rewarding. Before Carl was born, his twin sisters, Ellen May and Eileen Fay, were born prematurely in the Garkida hospital. One died during birth and the other one soon afterward. In a sad ceremony they buried the twin babies in the barren little cemetery where Stover's two wives had been laid to rest so many years before.

At one point, during the Shanksters' furlough to the United States, the Church of the Brethren ordained Owen and he became Reverend Shankster. He never liked the title and never introduced himself as such in Nigeria. Though Owen was responsible for a church or two here and there, he always felt his gift was not preaching. He was an engineer and a builder. And that is what he spent most of his time doing. During his forty years in northeast Nigeria, he helped dig over 2000 wells and engineer or build countless schools, clinics, and hospitals.

By far the biggest project Owen undertook was engineering and building Waka Schools, an immense school campus close to Biu. This school campus was approximately two miles long and a mile wide. It contained a primary school, a secondary school, a teachers' training college, and an enormous chapel. Student and staff quarters and all the buildings for classes, dining, and administration had to be planned, approved, and constructed. Mr. Quickly did it quickly, though he worked on the project off and on for seventeen years.

It was during the Waka School project that Mr. Quickly hired 200 Nigerians. As always, about half were Muslim. Again, they did their prayers. And again, Owen taught the Christians to put up with it and to work together in peace.

Waka Schools was funded by the Nigerian government, but once built, it was staffed and operated by the EYN. Eventually the schools were handed over to the Nigerian government.

Another thing that Mr. Quickly did quickly was name babies. Because of the high mortality rate, the Nigerians didn't bother to name their babies until they were two years old. After that, the mothers started hoping that the child would actually make it to adulthood, and they gave the baby a name. Soon the mothers found out that Mr. Quickly could name children quickly.

"Do you have a name for my baby?" they would ask him.

"Boy or girl?" was his quick response.

"Boy."

"Call him Chester."

And Chester he would be.

Or, "Girl."

"Call her Celia."

Celia she would be.

Mr. Quickly also got involved in settling disputes between villagers. He always had good advice on how to settle problems: quickly! Out of all his vocations, being a peacemaker was by far the most important one. And the example he and his family left in Garkida imprinted a distinct track in the corridor of time.

Back in Owen's time, Boko Haram didn't exist, but there was a lot of enmity between Christians and Muslims. The things Mr. Quickly exemplified and taught helped prepare the people for Boko Haram's eventual arrival. When they came, Mr. Quickly's example of living in love and peace was already there, ready to help the Garkida believers do quickly what Mr. Quickly had taught them.

Chapter 18

Under the Tamarind Tree Again

Ibrahim, Garkida's emir, hurried down the street in the dark, clutching his robe around his body. No stars shone that dark night, for a cloud bank was working its way over the town. The emir sensed it would rain soon. *What am I getting myself into?* His face clouded over with a troubled frown. *Why would Madamu send me such a strange message this late at night?*

Walking briskly through town, Ibrahim touched the slip of paper in his pocket as if hoping beyond hope that it would not be there and that the drama of the night was just a dream. In bold letters the note read, "Meet us under the tamarind tree tonight at midnight. Come alone and tell no one."

The name signed at the end of the note—Madamu—is what troubled Ibrahim the most. Madamu was an influential man in Garkida, and there had been rumors that he was supporting Boko Haram. *If that's the case,* Ibrahim worried, *this is not only a foolish venture, but also a dangerous one. What could Madamu want with me? And why did they ask me to come alone?*

The tamarind tree was a well-known landmark in Garkida. The immense tree stretched its broad branches across the rocky ground at the outskirts of town. Since it was dark, not even the people from the closest houses could see if folks met there. It was the perfect place to have a secret meeting.

The date was August 16, 2013.

As Ibrahim approached the rendezvous, a tiny red dot pierced the thick darkness under the tree's branches. *Someone is smoking,* Ibrahim thought warily as he stepped closer. Then a man cleared his throat.

"Good evening," Ibrahim said quietly, fear gripping his innards.

"Good evening," came the quiet response. Someone turned on a flashlight.

Ibrahim saw a huddle of six well-armed men waiting for him under the tree, dressed in military fatigues and sporting beards. *It is Boko Haram!* Ibrahim tried to calm his racing heart. Steeling his face, he marched on to meet the motley crew that awaited him.

"We called for you tonight because we need you," one of the Boko Haram soldiers announced. "We expect you to cooperate with us since you are a Muslim."

"What do you want me to do?"

"We plan to raid Garkida tomorrow night, and we want you to cooperate."

"What does that involve?" Ibrahim asked hesitantly, his mind racing a mile a minute, trying to figure out a way to stall these wicked plans.

"It's really simple," the obvious leader continued brusquely. "Just prepare a simple map of the town and mark which of the stores and houses belong to infidels. Also mark where the Christian churches are."

The silence that ensued was long and loud. Ibrahim was not prepared to answer such a horrific request. In that split second he realized how Boko Haram always managed to know who the Christians were and which houses and businesses to burn down. *It's always the emirs of the towns who sell their Christian friends. I can't do that!*

Somewhere from the depths of Ibrahim's kind heart, words tumbled out. "Look, my friends, you are right that I am a Muslim. But we have a problem here. In this town the Muslims and Christians have lived together in peace for forty years. I cannot and I will not help you destroy my friends' properties or have them killed."

"So you are a friend of the infidels?" the leader barked angrily. "A coward at heart."

"Please understand," Ibrahim answered softly, his whole body shaking in fear. "I am not a Christian, but in this town we have learned to live together in peace. We have become as one. We work together. We manage the city's affairs together. We run some of our businesses together. Our children study in the same schools. Muslims have married Christians. Christians have married Muslims. So how could I now turn against people who are at peace with me? I can't do it!"

The Boko Haram leader didn't say anything. The fact that he was silent spoke volumes. Ibrahim took courage and plunged on.

"Look," he said, "for many years foreign missionaries lived among us and taught us to live together in peace, to respect each other and work together. Because we have seen the benefits of living together in peace, I can't be a traitor tonight to people who are my friends, even if we don't believe the same."

Again silence reigned under the tamarind tree.

"That's why I am willing to run the risk of taking this stand. I know you want to burn the Christians' churches tomorrow night. If that's your plan, burn our mosque down first, because they helped us build it!"

Ibrahim's kind words for once melted the Boko Haram soldiers' hearts. Was it possible that such an example of peace between usual enemies struck a central chord and produced a longing for something every human yearns for?

The Boko Haram leader didn't make any promises. He didn't say if they would hit Garkida the next night or not. The conversation was over and the Boko Haram soldiers left, slipping out from under the tamarind tree silently.

Ibrahim walked the streets again, clutching his robe, his heart fluttering with all kinds of emotions. *Will my words move them? Will my tactics work? Will we all die tomorrow? Will the town be burned down? Time will tell.*

Eventually the truth came out, and everybody found out that Ibrahim was a hero. His gentle words had saved the town. That's why both times when Boko Haram hit Garkida they had mercy, and the destruction and killings were minimal.

Every Christian in town had a grateful heart. They thanked God again and again for a kind Muslim emir. They praised the Lord that the missionaries had taught them about love and nonresistance. And they thanked the Lord especially for His angel that encamped round about them and delivered them.

Chapter 19

The Hug of Death

I wonder where I'll find Mother, the skinny sixteen-year-old wondered as he pedaled his bicycle toward the army checkpoint outside Biu. *She'll probably be around the guard post where she often hangs out around noon.*

The bicycle was an old one, but Shadrach Daniel, who was good at tinkering, kept the rig going. On many occasions the bike had served as a second pair of feet. Today, for instance, his mother had called home and asked him to bring her lunch. Shadrach was right on the ball.

The sun was really hot and made the tarmac on the highway shimmer as Shadrach left the city of Biu and took the main highway toward the checkpoint.

Shadrach pedaled slowly. The little bag with his mother's lunch hung on one of the handlebars, swinging from side to side with the bike's momentum. As he pedaled, he was glad his mother had offered to help with the voluntary vigilance against the Boko Haram terrorists who were harassing all of northeast Nigeria. *Anything we can do to help is good,* he reasoned. *And even I am helping by carrying Mother her lunch.*

As Shadrach approached the roadblock, he could see a series of ramparts made of sandbags. They jutted out halfway across the highway. Each wall was placed strategically about every thirty feet, alternately jutting from both sides of the road, creating a maze that forced all drivers to slow down to weave through slowly. In the middle of the maze, and to one side of the road, stood a little hut that consisted of four posts planted in the ground. It was covered with coconut leaves to provide shade for the four soldiers who were stationed there. Every vehicle that came through was expected to stop, and a soldier would check to see if any Boko Haram terrorists were aboard.

The guards were trained to recognize the terrorists—by the way they dressed, by the way they acted, and especially by looking them straight in the eyes. The eyes of Boko Haram soldiers tended to dart around and show their nervousness. Since the government had set up several hundred such checkpoints on the main roads throughout the Northeast, almost no Boko Haram soldiers ever traveled on the main highways anymore. They knew they could get caught.

As usual, however, Boko Haram soon discovered ways to get around the authorities to carry out their atrocities. The soldiers paid little attention to people who walked through their checkpoints on foot. It might be farmers on their way to or from their fields of labor, women who needed to pass through on their errands, or children who came through in their work or play. People were walking in and out of Biu all the time. That's why the soldiers often only glanced at the pedestrians, nodding to allow them to pass through.

So when a man dressed like a poor farmer came walking down the highway that sweltering noonday, the soldiers paid little attention. They didn't notice that he was wearing a thick sweater on a hot day. But

Mami, Shadrach's mother, who was standing under a eucalyptus tree just beyond the guard post, became wary immediately. As the stranger approached her, she made some quick observations. The man wore the typical Boko Haram beard—long and straggly. His teeth were yellow. His clothes were dirty, as if he lived in the bush. And his leather sandals were torn and tattered.

Mami was part of a women's volunteer group that helped the army recognize any Boko Haram terrorists. For security reasons, the government constantly moved its soldiers around from city to city, and they seldom knew the locals. That's why local women were encouraged to hang around the guard posts to detect when strangers were about. And that's why Mami's antennae were twitching now. *He is not a local. He is a Boko Haram terrorist, and he is wearing a sweater because he is hiding a bomb. He is a suicide bomber!* As she realized the danger, her heart started to pound within her chest.

As she stepped out onto the highway to confront the man, she was worried. *Am I close enough to catch the soldiers' attention? If he is a Boko Haram, they have to move quickly to detain him or he will run.*

Glancing at the distant guards, she realized they did not notice her. They had been chatting some minutes earlier with a lady and her five children who were coming through the checkpoint. *This could get bad,* Mami realized. But she knew what she had to do, so she did it.

Shadrach was still pedaling slowly, three hundred feet away from the scene, when his mother confronted the terrorist. Oblivious of any danger, Shadrach was thinking about his plans for the afternoon. Up ahead, out of the corner of his eye, he saw a man walking down the road toward him, and then a woman stepping out to meet him.

When Mami stepped out into the Boko Haram soldier's path, she could see he wasn't happy. She also noticed that his hand crept up to his waist where she could detect a bulge under his sweater. She should have known better than to do what she did, but there was only one thing clear in her mind. *I have to stop this man before he goes into the city and kills a bunch of people.*

"Stop," Mami commanded. "Where are you going?"

The man stopped, close to the determined woman now. His eyes were crazed. Hoping against hope that the soldiers were watching, Mami continued, not taking her eyes off him. "Why are you wearing a sweater on such a hot day?"

The Boko Haram soldier now realized that Mami knew who he was. Thinking he had no other option, he jerked out his pistol and shot her in the stomach. Then he turned to run. Though Mami knew she was shot, she lunged and grabbed the soldier around the waist. "No, you don't!" she screamed.

By now the Nigerian soldiers were running toward them. As they came running, their AK-47s were poised and ready. The terrorist knew what would happen if they caught him. They would shoot him mercilessly for shooting an innocent lady. So he did what he was planning to do in the marketplace. He detonated the bomb that lay snuggled on his chest under the sweater.

It seemed as if the whole world blew up.

The soldiers fell backward because of the blast, but they were far enough away that they were in no danger of being killed. Shadrach was knocked off his bicycle, bruised, but not seriously injured. Things turned out far worse for the poor lady and her five children who had been approaching the place where the extremist had met Mami. They were killed instantly.

The explosion terrified poor Shadrach. Picking himself up off the ground, he pedaled home—a lot faster than he had come.

When Shadrach arrived at his grandparents' house, also the home of his only sister, fourteen-year-old Esther, he found everybody out on the street looking toward the distant roadblock, their eyes wide. But no one's eyes were as big as Shadrach's as he told them his frightening story.

"I don't know what happened!" he gasped. "I don't know what blew up, but the blast knocked me over and almost killed me!"

"Was it Boko Haram?" his grandmother asked, her eyes showing concern. "I hope your mother wasn't close by. Didn't you see her?"

"I am sure it has to do with Boko Haram," Shadrach confirmed. "But I wasn't paying any attention. I didn't see Mother, but there were some ladies and children up ahead, several hundred feet from where I was when the bomb went off."

Soon neighbors flocked around, and the questions about what had happened out on the highway grew by leaps and bounds. Shadrach was the center of attention as he showed them his bruises from his awful scare. He kept telling everybody that the explosion had almost killed him.

Esther was afraid to even voice it, but the question crying out in her heart was, *Where, oh where, is Mother?* It was then that a neighbor raced up, his eyes almost as big as Shadrach's had been. "It was Mami who was killed," he announced in anguish. "A suicide bomber killed her!"

En masse, the neighbors, along with Shadrach and Esther, raced to the scene of the bombing. Shadrach and Esther's hearts were breaking at the thought of their mother being blown up. But they had to know, so they ran with the rest.

What awaited them on the highway was almost beyond comprehension. As Shadrach and Esther mingled with the others, they were horror-struck by what had happened. There was a pool of blood where the bomb had gone off, and human limbs and body pieces were strewn around like sticks after a windstorm. The trunk of the closest eucalyptus tree was splattered with human flesh. But that was not the worst. The worst was hearing the soldiers from the checkpoint telling the gory details of the story again and again to everyone who came.

"Apparently Mami knew why that man was heading for the city!" the lead soldier narrated. "She knew if she didn't intervene, many people would die in the market or in the mosque. She died so that would not happen!"

The Hug of Death

That evening Shadrach and Esther sat in their grandparents' living room, sitting together on an old sofa, trying to find solace in each other. Their hearts were raw with pain, their eyes wet with tears. The neighbors had picked up some pieces of their mother's body and put them into a coffin that rested sadly in the corner of the room. "Now we are orphans!" Esther whispered to her brother. "Now we don't have a daddy or a mother."

Many years before, when Shadrach was three years old, and Esther was still in her mother's womb, their father, Daniel, had become sick and died. Shadrach had no memory of him at all. Over the years their mother had been extremely brave and had raised her two children the best she could in the midst of extreme poverty.

Shadrach remembered how he had helped make their living by selling sugarcane. He would get the long canes from his neighbor who had a plantation and had more than he wanted. Then Shadrach's mother would peel the juicy canes with a sharp machete and cut them into three-inch sections that he then peddled in town on his bicycle.

Shadrach had been living alone with his mother. He was her right-hand man whenever he wasn't studying. Esther, who lived with their grandparents, was also studying. And now, suddenly, they felt very alone. Crying softly, they comforted each other. "I guess God will take care of us," Esther whimpered. "God and Grandpa and Grandma."

Shadrach nodded. "Mother always taught us to pray. That's all we can do now."

Esther buried her face in her hands, and now she nodded, tears squeezing out between her fingers.

"Remember that time when Mother was so sick and we had no money to buy medicine?" Shadrach continued. "She told us to pray, and that same day one of our neighbors came and gave us money."

Esther nodded again, bringing her hands down on her lap. Shadrach noticed she was fondling something gold in her fingers. "Look what

Mother gave me the other day," she whispered through her tears.

Shadrach leaned forward eagerly.

"She was tired of wearing this ring, I guess," Esther replied, handing the small finger ring to her brother. "She told me to keep it."

"That's a beautiful keepsake," Shadrach sighed, fondling the ring just as Esther had. "Maybe Mother sensed that she was going to leave this earth and wanted you to have this token of her love."

Esther nodded, tears streaming down her cheeks.

"I guess what gives me courage to go on and to face life," Shadrach said, giving the ring back to his sister, "is the fact that Mother died to save so many others in our beloved city of Biu."

Smiling through her tears, Esther answered, "Yes, we'll never know how many people were saved today, all because Mother did what she knew was the right thing to do."

Chapter 20

Patience

*H*er skin was the color of creamy chocolate. Her teeth flashed white like newborn lambs whenever she smiled, which was quite often. Her hair was black, kinky, and usually covered with the typical African scarf. Her name was Patience.

Patience's father, Thomas Dawi, had christened her thus when she was born because, like most Nigerians, he believed the meaning of names was important. He had announced, "This tiny little girl's name will be Patience, because it takes a lot of patience to go through life."

Patience, the third in a family of eight children, was now twenty-two years old and as pretty as any Nigerian damsel in the northeastern city of Biu. Yes, it was no secret; Thomas was proud of his daughter.

On this memorable evening Patience and her family sat crowded in the living room. Suddenly she felt that somebody was staring at her. She turned quickly and caught her father gazing at her from the doorway to the parlor. She blushed slightly and wasn't at all surprised when he walked over to her, smiling broadly.

"Patience," he chuckled, "we are going to be so happy! Soon it will be your wedding day and we are going to celebrate!"

Patience threw back her head, laughing heartily. "Dad, you don't need a wedding to celebrate. You are always happy!"

Then, suddenly sobering, she added with a sigh, "Even though I am excited about getting married to Isaac, I am going to miss you all so much!"

Thomas was in a happy mood as he pranced across the living room and then back toward the kitchen. "Look at me, Mwada," he cheered. "Come see how I am going to dance on Patience's wedding day!"

Mwada, his wife and true love, came to the door, smiling. Placing her hands on her hips, she huffed, "If you keep hollering at me, I will never get this meal on. Of course we will be happy on her wedding day. Just contain yourself. It's still two months away."

"Dad, tell Patience about your new suit," Emmanuel said with a laugh. "She will be delighted."

Coming to a stop and turning abruptly to where Emmanuel sat, Thomas flashed a fake frown at his strapping seventeen-year-old, the baby of the family. "That's top secret!" he growled. "Be quiet!"

Patience dropped her face into her hands, laughing. *So he thinks that's a secret.* She had known for days that when she and Isaac were at the church getting pre-marriage counseling, her father had sneaked to town with her mom and had bought a new set of clothes. He had also bought wedding clothes for her and Isaac that day. *But that's neat that he still thinks it's a secret,* she thought, smiling to herself.

Just before Thomas exited for the parlor, and then on to the kitchen to harass Mwada, he paused to tweak Mala's ear.

Everybody in the family knew Mala was Thomas's favorite. None of the family resented it, because Mala was also everyone else's favorite. Mala was a Down syndrome child. Patience grinned as Mala smiled broadly, watching his father's antics. *His eyes are shining,* she thought. *He adores his daddy. God surely made him special!*

Arhyel, a 26-year-old who had at times taken his own way, was also smiling as he watched the scene. *I am so glad to be a part of this family!* He sighed, looking from one to the other. *We are such a close, happy family and are all excited about this upcoming wedding. And even if times are tough here in northeast Nigeria, we have each other as we face the future.*

Thomas had disappeared into the kitchen, and Patience was looking at her brothers now. Ibrahim, the oldest, sat in a corner chair. He was a quiet man, but with as solid a Christian faith as any. He was an inspiration in the church and was loved by all.

Next Patience looked at Arhyel. Love for him washed over her, and a tear sprang up in each eye. *Yes, he has made some poor choices in life and has caused Mom and Daddy so much heartache, but what a change he's made.* The rest of the family had always served the Lord in the EYN church, but from a young age Arhyel had taken his own way. It had caused much distress, especially for Thomas.

But just three weeks ago, a friend had invited Arhyel to a crusade given by the Foursquare Gospel Church in a neighboring town, and Arhyel had been converted. Thoroughly converted. *What makes me so happy is to see how happy this makes Mom and Daddy,* Patience cheered inwardly. *It has been such a boost for everyone to see God work in Arhyel's heart!*

But a dark cloud hung over the happy scene that evening. In fact, the gloomy haze hung over all Biu and northeast Nigeria. It was the fear and uncertainty created by Boko Haram. Their terrors had slowly but steadily crept south, and now had swung west, following the highway. Recently this band of terrorists had hit their own city of Biu, and terrible things had happened on the outskirts. A number of Christians had been ruthlessly killed, and businesses had been ransacked and churches burned to the ground.

I am so worried for Daddy, Patience cried inwardly, feeling her tender heart quake. *He is such a well-known figure in this town, and since he is an outstanding Christian, he is a target.*

There were several reasons why her father was a prime target for Boko Haram. One was that he was active in the local EYN church. Another was that, even though he was retired, he was still doing some work for the ministry of education. To Boko Haram, being part of the western education system was as big a crime as being a Christian. Also, her father was too friendly and popular to be able to hide in these hard times. *I am afraid some Muslim will sell him to Boko Haram for the love of money, or for envy.*

Thomas was standing at the door again as he announced, "The evening meal is ready. Let's gather to pray."

Just before the prayer, a knock on the door put a pause to the activities. A neighbor had stopped by to visit, which was nothing new in their home. "Come on in," Thomas insisted. "We are just ready to eat the evening meal. Come join us."

After the family and the visitor had gathered in the main room, they prayed, and then they all sat around the food that was served in large pots in the middle of a big rug. They squatted around the delicious meal of stewed goat and lentils, taking turns serving themselves from the steaming pots. Arhyel watched his father out of the corner of his eye. *Dad has such a big heart,* he mused, remembering what had happened that afternoon when he had gone with his father to buy bottled water at a nearby market. As they had slipped between makeshift stands, they had suddenly met up with a Muslim man whom Thomas had often helped.

He was a poor man who could never make ends meet. He had a large family and everybody knew his family almost never had enough food. Arhyel was not surprised when his father reached into his pocket and fished out several nairas and slipped them into Aamirah's hand. No one but Arhyel had seen the exchange.

"Thank you, thank you!" the man had gushed, bowing deeply.

Now, as they ate their meal, Arhyel noticed how much the neighbor man was enjoying himself. *That's why everybody loves Daddy. He is kind to everybody. Even the beggars love him. And no wonder.*

"Thanks so much for the meal, Mwada!" Thomas said, getting up off the floor once the meal was over.

"You are welcome," Mwada answered, grinning happily. "Did you have enough?"

"Almost ready to pop!" Thomas laughed, patting his belly. "You are the best cook in the world!"

Patience wished all her siblings were there that evening. Her older brother Dawi was traveling in the southern part of the country and wouldn't be back for several weeks. And two younger siblings, Isaiah and Sarah, were studying in boarding schools. Patience was excited about having the whole family together again for her wedding. *I can hardly wait!* she thought excitedly, a shiver racing up and down her spine. *Life is so good!*

An hour later everybody was in the living room except Mwada and Patience, who were washing the dishes and cleaning up the kitchen. Thomas was telling stories. Everybody knew Thomas was a storyteller, and often children and youth stopped by just to hear him. Now the neighbor and several of the family, especially Mala, were spellbound as they listened to his accounts.

Suddenly the spell was broken by a distant volley of gunshots. Their visitor jerked to attention. "Boko Haram?" he whispered.

"Oh, I doubt it," Thomas replied.

Mwada and Patience came rushing from the kitchen. "Did you hear those gunshots?" Mwada asked. "What do you think it was?"

"It's probably just the military," Thomas replied, trying to reassure everyone. "You know they have been doing that lately."

But soon there was more shooting. It seemed closer, and the faces in the living room turned pale. Suddenly all the joy and warmth fled the house and only a cold, raw fear remained, tugging at every heart. Boko Haram had never touched their haven, but all had heard of their atrocious acts in other parts of the city and throughout northeast Nigeria.

To see what was going on, Thomas slipped out the front door and sprinted to the courtyard gate. What he saw struck his heart with fear. There were people running down the dark street, all of them headed away from the volleys of gunshots. A few of the family had followed Thomas, and they and the visiting neighbor were soon looking over his shoulder. The visitor took one look, then slipped through the gate and disappeared into the gloom.

At that moment, Omana, a Muslim neighbor lady, came by. Thomas called out to ask her what was going on, but she ignored him and acted as if she hadn't heard. Thomas decided to lock the courtyard gate, then he and the others who had followed him outside returned to the house. All were wild-eyed in fear. "This does not look good!" Thomas told them, locking the front door securely. "Especially the fact that Omana couldn't face us. That really looks bad. I can hardly believe she'd sell us out to Boko Haram, but why else would she act so strangely?"

Patience nodded. "We have been so close to Omana's family over the last years. We do so many things together. But you are right, Daddy. If she refused to answer your question, something is wrong!"

"Shouldn't we run like everyone else?" Mwada asked, concern written all over her face.

"We are in God's hands," Thomas replied, looking at his wife tenderly. "Let's lock everything up and remain quiet. It will look as if we ran with the others."

After all had been sitting silently in the living room for a half hour, praying in their hearts, they heard their dog, Lampard, barking toward the back of the courtyard. The family froze. *What does that mean?* they all wondered.

The time was 9 p.m.

"I am afraid Lampard will draw attention to our house," Thomas said, admitting his fear. "Why don't we all go to bed and pretend no one is home?"

"Let's read a Psalm first," Mwada suggested. "I am afraid."

Thomas found his old, worn Bible and read Psalm 23 by the light of a candle. Then he led in a short prayer for protection, and everyone went to bed. Lampard was barking furiously now, running back and forth in front of the house. They could tell that someone had climbed over the wall and was moving around in the courtyard.

As Patience was sitting on her bed nervously, she could hear someone knocking on the front door. "Open up, Mr. Thomas," called a voice. "We need to talk to you."

"Do you think it's the military?" Mwada whispered, sitting on the bed beside her husband.

"No," Thomas answered, "the military wouldn't crawl over the wall. It's Boko Haram. And this is getting bad!"

Boom!

There was a loud whimper, and the whole family knew that Lampard was dead.

While the family prayed and quaked in their bedrooms, the Boko Haram terrorists began to get desperate. Not even trying to hide who they were anymore, they tried to shoot in the front door to get entrance. But the door was made of metal and the latch was high quality.

Next they shot out several windows. The glass shattered onto the floor, but since the windows had bars, they still couldn't get in.

An angry soldier approached the window to the living room and snarled, "Mr. Thomas, if you don't open for us, we will shoot your wife!"

Everybody in the house kept totally quiet. *Maybe they will think there is no one at home,* Patience thought as she sniffled into a hanky.

Thirty minutes passed as the soldiers tried to break into the house. As their shouts grew angrier and angrier, the hearts of the family grew more afraid. Thomas, especially, knew that unless God did a miracle, he would die that night. *Too bad the military shut off the phone service,* he thought ruefully. This had been done so Boko Haram couldn't communicate, but now there was no way Thomas could call anybody for help. *I guess only God can help us!*

Then another thought struck Thomas. They had a jug of gasoline out on the back porch. *What if they light up the house? They love to burn Christians' houses.*

Suddenly Arhyel was at their bedroom door, knocking gently. "Dad, open up."

Thomas opened.

With wide eyes and a pale face, Arhyel announced in an agitated whisper. "They lit the house! I first smelled the gasoline, and now I smell the smoke. Let's get together to pray."

By now Thomas was numb with fear. The realization that he was the target was heavy on him, and he suggested that Arhyel should lead the prayer. Arhyel took over and called all the family together in Patience's room, which was farthest from the fire.

By the time they were all huddled around in the center of the room, they could smell the smoke. The fire worked its way forward from the kitchen where they had first lit the house. The house was a concrete house with a tin roof, but there were two things that made the house burn well—the wooden framework in the roof and the plastic ceiling. The flames were eating up those like tinder. As the ceiling burned, it dripped down little dribbles that splattered the floor with hot melted plastic.

The Boko Haram soldiers had stopped trying to break into the house. They didn't want to brave the flames, and they knew that eventually the family would be flushed out. They just stood outside angrily, waiting on their prey.

By now the family started feeling the heat from the burning house and the smoke that wafted in through the door. "Let's pray," Arhyel gasped.

"We have to do something!"

Arhyel, who had been a Christian for only three weeks, was now the one who knew what to do. "We need to pray two prayers," he told them. "First, we need to confess any sin that we might have in our lives."

The family all knelt in a circle and held hands. Arhyel prayed for the forgiveness of any sins. He also claimed the blood of Christ for them all as he wept, pouring out his sincere heart to God. The rest prayed with him, most of them crying.

Then, lifting his tear-stained face, Arhyel added, "Now let's promise God that if they kill Daddy, or any of us, we will all be faithful till the end so that someday we can be together in heaven."

Again the family bowed their heads as Arhyel cried out to God. The message the young man prayed was heard, and the Heavenly Father wrote down the promise in His heart and gave the family a gift.

Once they got up from the prayer, their fear was gone.

"Let's stand here in a circle, holding hands as we burn," Arhyel suggested boldly.

"We can't do that," Thomas answered, shaking his head, "or we will all die. If we go out, some of you might live."

"But if we go out they will kill you, Daddy!" Patience wailed, clinging to her father's arm. "I don't want you to die!"

"But if we stay," Mwada replied, "he will die anyway. If we go out, maybe some of us would live."

By now the family knew they had to decide quickly. The raging heat from the fire was quickly engulfing Patience's bedroom where they were huddled. They could see the flames and feel its blast of heat. The smoke was choking them and they could hardly breathe. "We need to get out of here; the whole house is on fire!" Patience cried, for once forgetting to be quiet because of the soldiers. "I am choking to death!"

Again, Arhyel acted first. Whipping around the corner into the living room, with Ibrahim following, he saw a Boko Haram soldier looking in through the window. "Don't shoot!" he choked. "We are going to open up and come out."

The front door was jammed, and even jerking hard didn't budge it. Quickly Arhyel and Ibrahim sprinted to the other door on the opposite side of the living room. As soon as Arhyel touched the metal latch he knew it was too hot to touch without scorching his hand, so they raced back to the front door.

By this time, Arhyel and Ibrahim were in terrible pain. Not only were the heat and the smoke overwhelming them, especially their lungs, but the ceiling was dripping as it burned above them. When the little drips of burning plastic dropped on them, tiny holes burned through their shirts. By far the worst for the barefoot boys were the drops on the floor. It was like hopping around on a hot bed of lava. Every step they took around the living room was pure torture.

As Arhyel ran to the front door again, gasping for air, he prayed, "Lord, please help me open this door before it is too late!"

This time the door gave way, and a rush of fresh air gushed in.

The rest of the family, peering desperately from the bedroom door, rushed forward when the door opened, and everyone poured out onto the porch, gasping for breath. The soldiers had stepped back, heartlessly watching as they rushed outside. They knew their victims had chosen to face them because that was easier than burning alive in their own house.

As soon as they were all out, drinking in gulps of fresh air, a Boko Haram soldier commanded, "All of you come out into the yard and lie facedown. The women on this side." He pointed to his left. "And the men on the other."

Leaving the burning house behind, everyone obeyed.

Patience noticed that one of the guards had retreated and stood by the gate as if hiding behind the gate post. *We know him,* she guessed quickly. *He's trying to hide.* The other soldier stood in the open, giving orders, his dark face masked by a frown that drowned out any inkling of feeling or mercy.

As soon as the family was flat on the ground, the soldier stepped over to the man hiding beside the gate to consult what to do next. Patience started trembling all over when she heard the leader say quietly, "Shoot the men."

It was then that Thomas started to talk, his face flat on the bare ground in the courtyard. "Sirs, I know you will kill me. That's okay, but would you please spare the rest? Please have mercy on my family tonight."

The soldier was walking over toward them.

"The son I have in my arms has Down syndrome," Thomas continued in a pleading voice. "Please spare him. And the one on my other side is young. Spare him too."

Mwada's heart was torn to shreds. *Unless God intervenes,* she realized, *all my menfolk will be killed tonight.*

At that moment, she heard something that gave her courage. "Dear Father, I commit my life into your hands. Please help Daddy to be brave. Save Mala, dear Lord, and help Patience. And help me be faithful till the end."

Arhyel was praying. Quietly, yet audibly. Calmly, yet fervently. Suddenly the mother was comforted. *Even if my men die, they are ready to go.*

Neither Dad nor Arhyel are afraid anymore, Patience realized as she heard her father pleading for his sons and Arhyel praying to God. *The fear of death is gone.* The tender-hearted daughter's heart felt as if it could break for the men she loved so much. As she had gone down to the ground, in the light produced by the burning house, she noticed how the men were positioned. Arhyel was first in line. Then Ibrahim. Then her father, with his arm protectively around Mala, his special son. And last, young Emmanuel. *O Lord, protect Mala, please! And Emmanuel!*

The cold-blooded soldier's gun spoke three times.

Arhyel. Then Ibrahim. Then Thomas. Then the gun stopped. The soldier had seen that Emmanuel was young and Thomas's pleading voice had had its effect.

Mwada and Patience had rolled onto their sides when the shooting started to cautiously watch what was happening. Through the gloom they could see who was killed and who was spared.

Seeing that Arhyel was still alive, the soldier stepped back to the beginning of the lineup, and the gun spoke again.

Will Emmanuel be spared? Mwada and Patience's hearts froze as they waited.

It was time for Mwada to speak. In a bold voice, laced with Christ's love and following her husband's example, she lifted her head from the ground and pleaded, "You have killed my husband and my two oldest sons. God bless you! Thank you!"

The hush over that courtyard was a holy hush. The soldiers were caught off guard and were speechless. They didn't know what to do with love. Were their cold hearts stirred? Were they touched? Would it make a difference?

The brave woman continued her pleading. "Please spare my special son, and also the youngest. He is only a child."

Again silence reigned. The only thing Patience could hear was the crackling of the blaze that ate up their house and everything they owned.

The soldier stepped over to the gate and asked his boss, "What shall I do with the young one?"

The leader hissed, "Kill him! He is a man."

"But he is young," the soldier ventured hesitantly. "I saw his face."

Patience could tell that he pitied their mother. And maybe he even felt compassion for the strapping boy who lay trembling on the ground, his life hanging by a thread.

"He is only eighteen," the brave mother spoke up. "He is tall for his age. But he is the only one you are leaving me tonight besides the special one. Please let me keep him!"

The soldier turned and barked at Emmanuel. "Get up, young man!

Let's see how old you are."

Emmanuel unwrapped his long limbs and got up, slowly. He stood taller than his brothers and his father. He stood even taller than the two cowards who acted brave because they carried AK-47s. In the light of the flaming house, he stood there, an able, handsome young man of the kind only Africa can come up with.

"Kill him! He's a man," the leader snarled.

The soldier, however, had seen Emmanuel's young face and had heard the pleas of the loving mother. He had been greatly moved and couldn't do it. Stepping over to his boss, they deliberated. In a minute he was back and announced, "He will be spared."

Emmanuel took two quick steps over to where his mother sat weeping. Then he half bowed and half fell at her side. Putting his arm around her, he wept his tears into the dust of the courtyard. Patience was so overwhelmed she couldn't speak a word.

The soldier broke the spell by saying, "Tell the little boy to get away from his father."

Patience quickly peered over to see what was happening. What she saw broke her heart. Little Mala had realized that his father had been killed when that protective arm went limp, so he had gotten up and embraced his father's body protectively. His mind was too simple to know it was too late to protect his father now. Desperately he clung to his father, and Patience knew it would not be easy to get him off.

Nobody answered the soldier's command. Yelling at him, the soldier commanded, "Little boy, get off him!"

Mala didn't budge. No one was going to make him turn his precious father loose.

"Little boy, get up or I will shoot you too!" the soldier screamed.

Everything was quiet, and Mala might as well have been deaf or have been a statue.

After conferring with the boss, the hard-hearted soldier grabbed Mala by the arm and towed him away.

Mala didn't make a sound. But like Emmanuel, he crumpled down onto his mother's breast and wept his silent tears into her soul. Daddy would comfort him no more on this earth, but thank the merciful God in heaven that he still had his mother who would be there for him.

The Boko Haram soldiers now ordered all the survivors to leave the compound. Slowly Mwada and what was left of her family got up and headed for the gate, Patience taking the lead. Once again the leader of the operation backed off and hid so they wouldn't recognize who he was.

To Patience's surprise, a dozen Boko Haram soldiers were standing outside the gate on the street, apparently guarding the whole operation. There, a new leader made all of them lie down again, this time on the street. "Why didn't you open up for us right away?" the angry man complained, shining his flashlight at first one and then another. "You Christian infidels all deserve to die!"

"Where is your God now?" another soldier sneered. "Why doesn't He save you?"

No one answered the soldier's questions. Patience trembled as she felt the men's lecherous eyes drinking in her beauty in the light of the flashlight.

Growing tired of insulting the prostrate group, the soldiers stepped aside and deliberated what to do with the captives. They usually didn't kill the women and children, but they already had too many captives in the Sambisa, and Abubakar didn't want any more.

"Should we take them along?" Patience heard a voice ask in the background.

"But what would we do with them?" another voice wondered.

Please, Lord, was Patience's silent cry. *Don't let them take us. O Lord, have mercy.*

As several of the soldiers entered the courtyard again, wondering what to do with the bodies, a soldier appeared and asked the two ladies to follow them into the courtyard. "We want you to take the bodies away. We don't want people to be seeing these bodies here. Take them somewhere," the spokesman demanded.

Patience wished she had never followed the soldiers into the courtyard. What she saw was almost more than she could bear. They had shot Arhyel in the face and he looked horrible. She could barely recognize him. The men's feet and legs had been close to the flames and were blistered and scorched by the heat from the fire.

Patience's heart screamed. She closed her eyes and tried to shield her face from the heat with her hands. The worst of the fire was over, but low flames still licked up whatever was combustible on and around the brick walls of the house. *How can Mama take this? This is almost more than a person can handle!*

Patience was amazed, and her admiration for her mother soared when she heard her again pronouncing a blessing on the soldiers. "You killed my husband and my two sons. God allowed it. It is His will. God bless you. Thank you."

The horror of the night gripped Patience—body, soul, and spirit. Satan's horrendous work was seen so clearly on the three bodies lying in the courtyard, seared by the heat of the burning house. His demons were also clearly expressed in the faces of the heartless soldiers who stood staring at the ladies, the flames' flickering shadows on their dark, sinister faces. Again Patience closed her eyes to shut out the scene.

Suddenly the soldiers just wanted to get out of there. They had heard enough of Mwada's words of love in the face of hate. Did they feel the presence of a Holy God? Did they sense the arrival of God's almighty angels? Did the fear of the Lord fall upon them?

The two Boko Haram soldiers turned abruptly and left, as if in a stampede. They seemed scared by their own demonic acts and were desperate to leave. As the soldiers ran down the street with their cronies, they started shooting into the air to scare off any intruders.

Patience

Leaving the bodies at the scene, Mwada and Patience rushed out onto the street and found Mala and Emmanuel. They sat huddled on the sidewalk, waiting, not knowing what to expect. "They left," Mwada hissed, taking the lead. "Let's go to Mr. Genu's house. He will have pity on us."

It was a sad little group that rushed down the street in the dark of the horrible night. There was no moon, the night was dark, and they had no flashlights. Only the horrible memories of the awful night that still hadn't sunk in and the fear that continued to clutch at their hearts. *What if the Boko Haram soldiers come back? What if they start shooting again?*

Quickly they headed down the street to where Mr. Genu and his wife lived. After they knocked on the door, the fearful man opened it for them and ushered them into the living room. He was willing to do anything he could for Thomas's family. Mwada and Patience painfully told their story.

As the man left to look for church friends to make arrangements to move the bodies to a safer place, his wife ushered Mwada and her tribe into a bedroom where they could lie down on a bed and rest.

The boys lay on the floor. Mwada and Patience lay on the bed, but sleep was far away. As they lay there, they talked.

"I can't believe this is happening!" Patience whispered to her mother. "It just doesn't seem real. It's like a bad dream, and I want to wake up and find out it's not true."

"That's exactly what I am feeling," Mwada sighed. "I am in a daze. I guess it's because we are still in shock."

As they lay in silence, Patience wondered if the boys were sleeping.

Soon Patience heard her mother weeping again. "It doesn't seem real, Patience," she cried, "but we will never see Thomas, Ibrahim, and Arhyel again."

That's all it took for the dam to break. Reality hit young Patience, and she started crying out loud and screaming. Mwada hushed her up. "Please, Patience, hush!" she commanded. "Boko Haram might come back and hear us. Then they will kill us too!"

Patience soon got ahold of her emotions and quieted down. "Mom, I am going to miss them so much!" she wailed. "I don't know how life can go on without them."

Mwada wept unabashedly but quietly in the dark. "At least we know one thing," she exclaimed. "All three men are in heaven with Jesus."

"Right," Patience added, clinging to her mother in the dark. "I guess we should be glad for them. They were willing to die rather than to renounce Christ. I am sure God took them home, and that gives us great comfort, but it's still hard."

"We don't have to worry anymore for Thomas or for Ibrahim or for Arhyel," Mwada sighed, finding strength in her daughter. "We know where they are right now. We just need to be faithful so we can soon be with them."

"If I die," Patience continued, tears streaming down her face, "I want to die like they did. We need to strive to follow their path so we can all be together in heaven. Oh, I wish I were there right now!"

A few weeks later, when Patience's brothers Dawi and Isaiah came home again, they all cried and cried as they retold the story. Finally Mwada took hold of their hands and said, "Cry no more, for we do have some good news. Your dad and brothers are resting in the Lord. They didn't renounce their faith even at the point of death. I hope you would do the same."

Acknowledgments

The dining room was small, but the table in the center was ample. Big enough to accommodate nine people—and some good food. The table was surrounded by a circle of smiling faces. The place was Englewood, Ohio, and our kind hosts were Carl and Roxane Hill. We were there to talk about the possibility of compiling a book of testimonies of the suffering Christians in northeastern Nigeria, especially Christians from the EYN churches.

The group of friendly Americanos made my wife and me, fresh from the boonies of Waslala, Nicaragua, feel right at home. Though I was supposedly the writer for the proposed book of Nigerian testimonies, I knew the project needed teamwork. And a big part of that team was sitting right there at the table.

Carl and Roxane, who sat to our right, were very familiar with northeast Nigeria. Roxane's family had moved to Garkida, an area we would focus on, as missionaries when she was just a year old. She lived there the first eighteen years of her life. Her father, Ralph Royer, was an educator and part of the Church of the Brethren school efforts. He was also a lover of trees and oversaw the planting of many of the trees standing in Garkida today.

After coming back to the U.S., Roxane married Carl, and since then they have been involved in taking aid to the Nigerian people. Carl and Roxane usually travel to Nigeria several times a year delivering aid. Their knowledge of Garkida and the surrounding areas was a very valuable part of the research for this project. Also of great help was their knowledge of the history of the Church of the Brethren, as well as giving us leads to many potential contacts. Thanks so much, Carl and Roxane, for your invaluable help!

Down at the end of the table sat jolly Carl Shankster from Silver Lake, Indiana. Though he and his wife are not Church of the Brethren anymore, but are part of the German Baptist Church, Carl grew up in northeast Nigeria in a Church of the Brethren mission. For that reason, Carl was an important part of preparing for my trip to Nigeria. Not only does he have eighteen years of firsthand experience living in Garkida, but he is also a master storyteller. We heard many exciting stories around the table that memorable day in Englewood—some of which found their way into this book.

Carl's father was the builder and handyman whom everyone called Mr. Quickly, because that's the way he was. He wanted everything done well—and quickly.

On the left side of the table sat Reuben Shankster, Carl's son, who has also traveled to Nigeria several times. On the day of the interview, he was dressed in a Nigerian robe and cap. We became friends fast. Though a bachelor, he did a wonderful job of hosting my wife and me for the two days we were in the area. Thanks to all of you Shanksters for your help in making *No Turning Back* a reality.

On the left side of the table, next to Reuben, sat Alvin Mast, head of the Research and Development Department for TGS, CAM's branch that prints their books. Beside him sat Steve Leid, his helper. They came to the meeting to give suggestions and support for the project. Thanks, Alvin and Steve, for your helpful advice and direction!

After flying for what seemed like forever, my wife and I landed in Abuja, Nigeria. We were hot, bone-tired, and felt more than a little lost. Walking up to baggage claim, wondering where to go next, we met a tall, black-bearded man who looked a little like Abraham Lincoln. As he smiled at us broadly, we felt ourselves relaxing. Trent Eikenberry and his delightful family, who work with CAM's SALT program, were there to meet us. For the next two weeks, they took us into their hearts and home. Words fail to describe the wonderful time we had with them.

Trent and his son Carter took us on a trip into northeast Nigeria where we did most of the research for this book. Trent's knowledge of the African culture and the Nigerian ways was such a vital part of this venture. He also knew of so many possible contacts. Dear Trent and family, we thank you from the bottom of our hearts for your wonderful contribution to *No Turning Back!*

After we met Trent at the airport, we headed to the parking area after claiming our luggage. A young Nigerian fellow cuddled up to me and purred, "May I help you with your luggage?"

I rudely clung to my suitcase and snapped, "I can handle it."

We have those fellows in Nicaragua as well, I thought to myself. *Always offering to help, then expecting to be paid for their services.*

Fortunately Trent caught on what was happening. "By the way," he announced, pointing at the annoying youth, "this young man is Chinna. He is one of our drivers and will be one of your translators."

I apologized profusely and allowed Chinna to take my suitcase. We soon became the best of friends.

Joshua was also a great help during our time in Nigeria. His story, "A

Deep, Deep Sleep," has become one of the many testimonies in this book.

Thank you, Chinna and Joshua, you were much more than excellent translators and guides—you became our blood brothers and devoted friends!

Finally, I want to thank all of you Nigerian Christians for the way you took us foreigners into your hearts. Though you were a little timid at first, you ended up telling us your heartfelt stories freely. My wife and I found it such a blessing to cry and pray with each one of you as you shared your stories. May God bless you.

"No turning back, no turning back!"

About the Author

Pablo lives with his wife Euni and two of their children, Janie and Kenny, in Waslala, Nicaragua, where he serves as an evangelist and a bishop of a local congregation. Four of their oldest children are married and are scattered as far as Costa Rica and Brazil.

Pablo is a prolific writer and has written more than a dozen books, many of them biographies. He tries to write a book a year if possible.

Pablo also enjoys many hobbies. His house is surrounded by an orchid collection growing on the many varieties of trees he has planted. A pond next to the house attracts many species of birds and other wildlife. If you visit Pablo's home, he'll take you on a tour to see his orchids, play with his pet howler monkey, and feed Herod, his pet alligator in the pond. In fact, you can't really get to know Pablo without hearing him talk about nature—and the Creator who crafted it.

If you would like to know more about Pablo and his family, read *Home on the Rock Pile, Home on the Blue Ridge, The Long Road Home, Angels Over Waslala,* and its sequel, *Angels in the Night.* These and most of the other books Pablo wrote are available from Christian Aid Ministries. His three nature books—*The Work of Thy Fingers, The Work of His Hands,* and *My Father's World*—are also available from CAM.

Pablo enjoys hearing from readers and can be contacted at pabloeuni@gmail.com or written to in care of Christian Aid Ministries, P.O. Box 360, Berlin, Ohio 44610.

About Christian Aid Ministries

*C*hristian Aid Ministries was founded in 1981 as a nonprofit, tax-exempt 501(c)(3) organization. Its primary purpose is to provide a trustworthy and efficient channel for Amish, Mennonite, and other conservative Anabaptist groups and individuals to minister to physical and spiritual needs around the world. This is in response to the command to ". . . do good unto all men, especially unto them who are of the household of faith" (Galatians 6:10).

Each year, CAM supporters provide 15–20 million pounds of food, clothing, medicines, seeds, Bibles, Bible story books, and other Christian literature for needy people. Most of the aid goes to orphans and Christian families. Supporters' funds also help to clean up and rebuild for natural disaster victims, put up Gospel billboards in the U.S., support several church-planting efforts, operate two medical clinics, and provide resources for needy families to make their own living. CAM's main purposes for providing aid are to help and encourage God's people and bring the Gospel to a lost and dying world.

CAM has staff, warehouses, and distribution networks in Romania, Moldova, Ukraine, Haiti, Nicaragua, Liberia, Israel, and Kenya. Aside from management, supervisory personnel, and bookkeeping operations, volunteers do most of the work at CAM locations. Each year, volunteers at our warehouses, field bases, Disaster Response Services projects, and other locations donate over 200,000 hours of work.

CAM's ultimate purpose is to glorify God and help enlarge His kingdom. ". . . whatsoever ye do, do all to the glory of God" (1 Corinthians 10:31).